The World at Their

The Story of Electra House and its Overseas Telegraph Operators and Their Role in World Telegraphy

Geoff Boudreau

Backtrack Rye

First published in Great Britain by Backtrack, Rye in 2018

© Geoff Boudreau

ISBN: 978-0-9957144-0-3

Printed in Great Britain by Adams of Rye

for

Keith Ward, Paul Todd and Derek Worster

— fellow travellers who left the party early —

Contents

Acknowledgements:

The author would like to thank the following for their invaluable contributions to the production of this book:

Richard Cannon, Colin Entacott, Jim Grant, Joan Heaford, Chris Hicks, Val Hopkins, George Hopwood, Bob Jarrold, Stan Mansfield, Pete Norris, Peter Nutt, Dave Parry, Jack Pennington, Eileen Pollard, Susie Sells, Dennis Wood, Mike Zacsinsky, the BT Archive, Holborn, Peter Fisher of the London Metropolitan University Archive and Charlotte Todd and Rudy Topsey of the Telegraph Museum, Porthcurno.

Thanks too to Ellen Church for the cover and map designs.

I also give special thanks to my editor, Ron Shepherd, whose support and patience helped make this book possible.

(Electra House, Victoria Embankment)

Introduction

This book strives to document the history of Electra House, Victoria Embankment, which for a period of some sixty years served as the major centre of world telegraphy. It is also the story of its predecessor, also named Electra House, situated at Moorgate, which operated between 1902 and 1941. In addition, the story covers the development of the technology, the systems and machines that made it all possible, and the Overseas Telegraph Operators who worked those systems day in, day out, unsung heroes of the world of communications. The story would not be complete without the inclusion of the other related London telegraph offices from over the past century.

Electra House, situated in the WC2 postal district (later WC2R 3HL), was built between 1929 and 1931 as the headquarters of Cable and Wireless Ltd. and continued in use until 1989 under that company's UK successors, Post Office Overseas Telegraphs, British Telecom, and finally British Telecom International, as the world's 'clearing house' for telegraphic traffic. The book also explores the fascinating history of the buildings and the central London sites they occupied.

The story of these iconic buildings also has to be put in context in the history and evolution of the telegraph stretching back over 200 years, a tale of triumph and failure, of heartbreak and success.

This is also the story of the people who's inventions made telegraphy possible, the entrepreneurs who put their faith and often their finances on the line in pursuit of a dream, the engineers who designed and kept systems and machines running, often against the odds, and last but not least, the day-to-day telegraphers or telegraphists as they later became known, who operated the systems to send and receive telegrams from around the world – messages of congratulation and condolence, of breaking news or of urgent business information.

In these days of high-speed broadband technology, the Internet and the World Wide Web, it's easy to forget the giant strides made over the past two centuries, which paved the way for the modern world of instant high-speed communication by satellite, computer and mobile telephone.

Chapter One

From Morse to Marconi – The Origins of Telegraphy

'The World at Your Fingertips' is a phrase that has been with us for a long time and it has been used by many organisations over the years, but by none more appropriately perhaps than the Overseas Telegraph Operators sending and receiving telegrams from around the world, whether they be the bearers of glad tidings or sad news, vital information and perhaps messages of international significance or just day-to-day trivia. For over 150 years the telegram brought people closer together, bringing perhaps joy one minute and dread the next, but always bridging the gap between people, often of thousands of miles, to impart important information as quickly as possible.

Electra House, on London's Victoria Embankment, looking south over the River Thames, was in its heyday, stretching over six decades, to play a significant role as the world centre for international telegraphy and telegrams.

It housed London Station, the head office of Cable and Wireless and the hub for many of the world's international telegraphic links. To fully understand its place in the history of telegraphy we must go back in time some 200 years to trace the development of the telegraph and its subsequent use initially via both landlines and undersea cables, and later by wireless. In addition we'll explore the buildings and systems, which preceded and followed it as society adjusted to each new generation of communications technology and the company expanded to accommodate the needs of its customers in an ever-changing world.

But to put things in context, we must go all the way back to the invention of the first practical working telegraph system, which is generally credited to Samuel F. B. Morse (1791–1872) in 1837, the first year of Queen Victoria's reign.

Prior to the development of electric telegraphy, there were several systems of conveying simple messages on land over any distance not involving a runner or a horse messenger such as with the Pony Express. If we discount Stentor, who according to Homer, writing in *The Iliad*, claimed "his voice was as powerful as fifty voices of other men", perhaps the earliest would have been the use of carrier pigeons, recorded as early as 2,500 years ago to announce victories at the Olympic Games at Olympia in Ancient Greece. Stentor, by the

(Samuel Finley Breese Morse)

way, was reputed to have died after a shouting contest with Hermes, or Mercury as the Romans renamed him. Otherwise trumpets on a battlefield could convey a limited range of commands within perhaps a three mile radius.

The use of carrier pigeons has continued through history to the present day but with various drawbacks in their use, as birds could be affected by adverse weather conditions or fatigue or perhaps snared en route to their destination. Beacons and signal fires as means of communication also have a long history, a chain of which famously carried news of the approach of the Spanish Armada along the English Channel in 1588. In addition the Royal Navy had a long tradition, dating back to the 14th century of using semaphore flags to signal from ship to ship and ship to shore, but it wasn't until more recent times that more reliable systems were used.

Messages by sea from England to its overseas colonies and trading interests could take many months to reach far-flung destinations although this was vastlyimproved when the Packet Service was introduced in 1688. It was instituted by The Post Office who chartered ships to sail out of Falmouth in southern Cornwall to destinations in North and South America as well as to the Mediterranean. The ships were to carry passengers in addition to mail, to improve the financial viability of the service. The system was to run until the 1850s, by which time electric telegraphy via undersea cables was preparing to take over.

The use of the heliograph, using a mirror to direct light from the sun at a distant point, is first credited to a German professor, Carl Friedrich Gauss, who invented its predecessor, the Heliotrope in 1821. It focused a controlled beam of sunlight on a distant observer, but was of course restricted to use during daylight and not practical under cloudy conditions.

Already in use at that time was the semaphore system using the optical telegraph invented in 1791 by Frenchman Claude Chappé who named his

(Chappé's semaphore system, the wonder of its age)

invention the *télégraphe,* the term deriving from the Greek *tele, '*at a distance' or 'afar' and from *grapho* – 'to write'. (Interestingly, the term 'television' was of mixed parentage, 'tele' from Greek and 'vision' from the Latin verb *videre,* 'to see', something which no doubt would have evoked indignant letters at the time to the editor of *The Times*!). Chappé's system consisted of moveable black and white arms mounted on towers in line-of-sight, the position of the arms denoting the relevant letter or figure being 'transmitted'. Using telescopes on a clear day, a message could be read, deciphered and re-transmitted along a relay of towers on to its destination. The new French Revolutionary government saw the value of the system and in 1794 a line of 15 towers was constructed to connect the 130 miles between Paris and Lille in the north of the country. Further rapid expansion quickly followed and France was to show the way forward to the rest of Europe.

The Admiralty in London was not slow to appreciate the value of such a system and amid increasing fears of a French invasion of England by Napoléon in the 1790s and early 1800s, they ordered the construction of a line of towers from the capital down to the south coast using a 'shutter system'. This system, invented in 1795 by the Reverend Lord George Murray, used six shutters in two columns in a vertical frame and allowed for 64 different permutations. He was awarded the considerable sum of £2,000 for his invention and was made Superintendent of Telegraphs with the then substantial salary of £300 per annum.

By Nelson's day a signal could be sent from the roof of the Admiralty building at Whitehall in London, via a series of relay stations in line-of-sight approximately eight miles apart, to reach the naval ports of Portsmouth and Plymouth (opened in May 1806) in the south-west, or south east to Deal in Kent (the first connection to be completed) or to Great Yarmouth in Suffolk up on the east coast. It was said that with good visibility a signal could be sent or received between London and the coastal stations in a matter of minutes.

By 1822 the Admiralty had replaced the shutter design with the simpler semaphore system. It was designed by the unlikely named Sir Home Riggs Popham and had been approved by Parliament in 1814.

Both visual systems depended on favourable weather conditions or access to sunlight and were limited in the amount of information they could convey and the speed of conveying it. As recognition of the power and potential of electricity began to take place in the 1800s, it was soon realised that systems harnessing that power represented the way forward.

(The London Admiralty building displaying an early Semaphore system)

In September 1831, after considerable work had been done to extend the semaphore system around the south of England, further expansion plans were shelved, as early experiments taking place with the new electric telegraphy made it clear to the government where the future lay. It was in fact with telegraphy that the first practical use of electricity would be, many years before the invention of the light bulb or the telephone.

Many researchers, including Joseph Henry (1797-1878) in America, Samuel Sömmerling (1755-1830) in Germany, and William Cooke (1806-1879) and Charles Wheatstone (1802-1875) in Britain, had worked on similar projects prior to Morse, but his instrument was the first to send messages any substantial distance via wires using electricity. Since 1832, when Morse had witnessed Charles Thomas Jackson demonstrating experiments in electro-magnetism on a transatlantic voyage he had worked on the project with Leonard Gale (1800-1883) and in close conjunction with Alfred Vail (1807-1859). Where Morse succeeded and others failed was in his ability to send a signal any distance along a wire without it fading badly. The key to the problem was to use a series of small batteries in line with an electro-magnet, rather than one large battery, a solution in fact already successfully worked out by Joseph Henry.

The system Morse developed used an electrical circuit and an overhead wire, using the Earth as the other conductor to complete the circuit. An electro-magnet at the receiving end could be activated by completing, then breaking the circuit, producing distinctive clicks, resulting in what became known as 'Morse Code'. The familiar code of dots and dashes, still in daily use today, then enabled people to potentially send messages across great distances in an instant, or to be exact at the speed of light, 186,000 miles per second, when previously perhaps it would take days, weeks or even months by horse or ship to deliver an urgent message.

Morse, also a highly accomplished portrait painter, patented his device in 1840 and on May 24th, 1844 sent the first message from Washington, D.C. to Baltimore, Maryland, a distance of some 36 miles. The message sent, a biblical quotation from the Book of Numbers, read '*What hath God wrought*'.

He and Alfred Vail were the first two operators of the system, and Vail was to go on to develop and run several new telegraph lines between 1845 and 1848, before quitting as superintendent of the Washington and New Orleans Telegraph Company as he could not live on his $900 a year salary. In resigning, he wrote to Morse to say "I have made up my mind to leave the Telegraph to take care of itself, since it cannot take care of me...". Vail retained his one-eighth share in Morse's patents, and spent the last decade of his life conducting genealogical research.

Even after successfully demonstrating the invention to the American government there was still scepticism and distrust for the device but Morse persevered and eventually the vast potential of what he was advocating was recognised by both Washington and the world of commerce, and substantial investment in the technology followed. Within a few years 2,000 miles of telegraphic wire was reaching out across the United States, and this figure rose to 12,000 by 1850. The rapid spread of the telegraph system continued between major U.S. cities, culminating in a trans-continental wire which was completed 24th October 1861, effectively signalling the demise of the Pony Express system.

In the early days of telegraphy a simplex system operated, whereby a single signal was sent in one direction and when the line was clear, a reply could be sent back, but by 1854 a duplex system was patented, allowing simultaneous two-way traffic. Further refinements and improvements followed later with Thomas Alva Edison, that giant of the late Victorian age, inventing the quadruplex system, whereby four signals, two in each direction could be sent over the same wire at the same time. He sold his invention in 1874 to the Western Union Company for the not inconsiderable sum of $100,000.

Meanwhile across the Atlantic, the system which Cooke and Wheatstone had patented in 1837, was limited to working across dry land. Their original device used a five needle system set in a diamond shaped grid, whereby the vertically-set needles could move diagonally left or right – the movement of two needles indicating a letter of the alphabet. Sadly, the two men formed an uneasy partnership from the start and for the rest of their lives disputed each other's contribution to the invention of their telegraph, although there was some measure of 'putting the matter to rest' when after attending Wheatstone's funeral in 1875, Cooke's recollection of events admitted Wheatstone's major role in the development of the telegraph.

In 1846 the Electric Telegraph Company was formed by Cooke and John Lewis Ricardo, a Member of Parliament and a prominent financier. The company bought out the patent rights from Cooke and Wheatstone and it went on to become the most successful private telegraph company in Britain with 10,000 miles of line by 1868, primarily running alongside the burgeoning Victorian railway network. The company merged with the International Telegraph Company in 1855 to become the Electric and International Telegraph Company, which was later, in 1870, to be nationalised by the British Post Office.

But back in the late 1830s and early 1840s considerable efforts were being made to find a solution as to how to carry a signal via an undersea cable. As early as 1795 a Spaniard, Señor Salva, had suggested the feasibility of submarine telegraphy in a paper read to the Barcelona Academy of Sciences, but theory is one thing and the practicality of realising the dream was another, with tremendous difficulties to overcome first.

The first record of practical underwater telegraphy is credited to Colonel C. W. Pasley of the Royal Engineers at Chatham in northern Kent in 1838 but it wasn't until 1850 that a substantial practical working system was laid when the brothers Jacob and John Watkins Brett briefly spanned the Straits of Dover between England and France, with their cable. A year later the Submarine Telegraph was successfully laid across the English Channel and demonstrated in the presence of the Duke of Wellington, the then Lord Warden of the Cinque

Ports, the ancient confederation of English Channel ports of which Dover was one. The man behind the enterprise was a 36 year-old Scot, John Pender, who was destined to play an increasingly important role in the spread of submarine telegraphy around the world.

Pender, born in 1816, the year after Wellington's famous victory over Napoléon at Waterloo, was the son of a middle-class Scotsman. He was educated at Dumbarton and Glasgow and started work in the counting house of a local factory. Coming from a family of bleachers and textile workers, he rose at the tender age of 21 to become the managing director of the company he worked for. Moving to Glasgow in 1840 he married a local girl, Marion Cearns, who tragically died a year later whilst giving birth to their first child. In his grief, Pender threw himself into his work and quickly established himself in Glasgow as a successful cotton merchant, mainly trading with companies in India during the 1840s.

Interestingly, at this time another person taking a keen interest in the new telegraphy was one Charles Dickens, who came up with an idea for a story 'bringing together two strongly contrasted places and two strongly contrasted sets of people through the agency of an electric message'. In the December 1850 edition of *Household Words*, he described his visit to the central telegraph station of the South-East Company based at Tonbridge in Kent, and went on to give practical, albeit simplified details of the workings of the company's system for his readers.

Now that the Straits of Dover had been successfully spanned, eyes were turned to the prospect of bridging the 60 miles between England and Ireland, and the English and Irish Magnetic Company was formed to pursue the idea. William Cooke's Electric Telegraph Company had the monopoly in Britain but this was increasingly being challenged. Meanwhile, two attempts, by Stirling Newall, to lay submarine cables across the Irish Sea in 1851 and 1852 had failed, but the British and Irish Magnetic Company were not discouraged and in June 1852 set out to lay their own cable, providing a link between the Home Office in London and The Castle, Dublin, the seat of the British government's administration in Ireland. John Pender who had by then become relatively wealthy, not least due to the large dowry brought to him through his second marriage, to Emma Denison, was attracted to fund the project, further fuelling his lifelong interest in, and obsession with submarine telegraphy.

The chief engineer for the British and Irish Magnetic Company was Charles Bright and his work ensured that the cable laid in May 1853 between

Portpatrick in Scotland and Donaghadee in County Down, Northern Ireland was well made and built to last. The company also successfully laid another cable from Portpatrick to Whitehead, near Donaghadee. Later, in 1870 both cables were taken over by the British or General Post Office (GPO).

One person quick to recognise the commercial potential of the cross-Channel and Irish telegraph links was Paul Julius Reuter who had set up his fledgling news agency in the 1840s in his native Germany, albeit with the use of carrier pigeons. He relocated to London in 1851 and was to exploit the new submarine cable links, not least from Ireland where ships arriving from America would throw canisters containing news and financial information into the sea for collection and onward transmission to London.

Work on other telegraph lines in many other countries soon followed and by the mid 1850s the Morse system and apparatus had been adopted around mainland Europe and it was estimated at that time that there were some 8,000 miles in operation in Europe as a whole, more than half operated by the Electric Telegraph Company and a quarter by the English and Irish Magnetic Company. Governments and the public alike marvelled at the speed of communication when in 1855 the news of the death of Tsar Nicholas I of Russia in St. Petersburg was received and announced in London at the House of Lords just a few hours after it occurred. It was also becoming increasingly clear that the future lay with the Morse system and at a banquet in London in 1856 to honour Morse, Cooke was happy to admit the fact.

At this time many people thought it too daunting and expensive a task to consider linking Europe with North America by undersea cable but there was a plan to make the link through Europe overland via Siberia and then across the 100 miles of the Bering Strait to Alaska, which could then link to the continental United States. At this time Alaska was owned by Russia and the Imperial Russian government agreed to consider the idea. Meanwhile in Nova Scotia an English emigrant, F. N. Gisborne had acquired a 50-year charter to link Newfoundland with New York but due to lack of funding had sold his interest to a wealthy New York paper merchant named Cyrus Field. Field, although no engineer had the vision and imagination to envisage such a system continuing on from Newfoundland to Britain.

Finding the raising of capital for the project too difficult in the United States, he sailed to London to meet John Brett, who had experienced similar fund raising problems a few years earlier when planning his cross-Channel cable. He found a better reception from investors in England and formed the

Atlantic Telegraph Company in 1856 to which he transferred his charter. One of the 345 English investors was one John Pender then based in Manchester. At the first meeting of the new company in December 1856 Pender was made a director of the new company.

Thereafter 3,750 miles of armoured cable with Gutta Percha insulation were ordered for the project. Gutta Percha (Palaquium), which was discovered by Dr. William Montgomery in 1843, was produced from the inelastic latex of the Gutta Percha tree, a native of South East Asia and had been used to produce golf balls since 1848. It was the best-known product available for submarine use in insulating the copper cable and being light enough to transport on cable ships. Signals would be sent along the cable, stopping and starting the flow using a rocking-action 'Morse' key utilising Samuel Morse's code. Substantial subsidies were made available from both British and American governments, who realised the major importance of such instant communication.

The company's first attempt to lay the cable in August 1857 met with failure, with the loss of over 1,000 miles of cable, when it parted at 2,050 fathoms, or 2.3 miles, below the surface. As a result the chairman of the Atlantic Telegraph Company, Sir William Brown, wanted to abandon the project and refund investors' capital but Cyrus Field had not come so far to give up now and with the support of John Pender and others insisted they try again. They still had over 2,000 miles of cable and a 'Telegraph Squadron' of specially adapted naval vessels at their disposal. It was make or break time as the vessels would soon have to return to official duty and might not be offered again. The second attempt commenced on 17th July 1858 and on 13th August transatlantic communication was established for the first time, although it took sixteen hours for Queen Victoria's 98-word message to President Buchanan to be sent. Contact was improved and before long, messages took mere minutes rather than hours.

The connection was heralded on both sides of the Atlantic as the great innovation it surely was and over 150 years later it is still heralded as an amazing feat of technology. Suddenly news of events thousands of miles away could be transmitted virtually instantaneously and more importantly, to some people, financial information could be sent and received and investments could be made from afar.

Unfortunately the celebrations over the laying of the transatlantic link were short-lived, as the signals sent along the cable, never very strong, got progressively weaker due to a fault in the insulation off the coast of Ireland.

Despite raising the battery power, the signal continued to degrade and finally by 18th September it disappeared entirely after a mere five weeks of operation in which it carried 732 messages.

In addition to the failure of the transatlantic cable, an attempt to link Britain with the Far East, a project of the Red Sea and Telegraph to India Company, also failed and the plan was abandoned. As the British government had heavily invested in both projects a committee of enquiry was set up in 1859, on the '*Construction of Submarine Telegraph Cables*' under Captain Douglas Galton, of the Royal Engineers. The committee's findings concluded that submarine telegraphy was not as straightforward as had been thought and there was much still to learn. In an attempt to provide a platform for knowledge to be shared, John Pender and others went on to establish *The Telegraphic Journal*. The sixpenny weekly later changed its name to *Electrical Review*, which has survived to the present day.

Despite the failure of such major projects and the loss of almost all the £460,000 paid-up capital invested in the Atlantic Telegraph Company, it remained in existence and a new Act of Parliament, which become operative in 1859 gave the company authority to raise up to £2 million for a future project. Understandably it was going to be difficult to convince investors to part with their money in the light of recent failures and the British government was approached to offer a financial guarantee and despite the initial rejection of the application, a guarantee of £600,000 was later agreed, conditional on a new transatlantic cable being successfully laid and working. The U.S. government then agreed to a similar guarantee.

At that time, as rulers of such a far-flung empire, the British government needed no reminding of the vital importance of linking London to the colonies, especially in the Far East. As commercial attempts to lay submarine cables had been less than successful, the government decided itself in 1859 to commission the manufacture and laying of a cable from Falmouth in Cornwall in the south west, to its strategically important naval base at Gibraltar, guarding the entrance to the Mediterranean. However, due to the then war against China it was decided to use the cable between Rangoon in Burma and Singapore instead.

Before the laying of the cable could be completed, the war had ended, although the handling of the Indian Mutiny of 1857 without a means of direct communication had highlighted the urgent need for connecting London with India and beyond. This link was finally established in January 1865 via a mixture of landlines and submarine cables, via Constantinople (now Istanbul) and Persia (now Iran) to Karachi (now in Pakistan) to link with the existing telegraph system courtesy of the Indo-European Telegraph Department.

Meanwhile, in 1862 the Atlantic Telegraph Company, spearheaded by John Pender, now the Member of Parliament for Totnes in Devon, used the authority of the 1859 bill to raise capital and issued a prospectus to raise the £600,000 for the next transatlantic cable. By May 1863 £300,000 of the amount required had been raised. By that time the main cable makers, Glass, Elliott of Greenwich and Gutta Percha of Stratford had perfected cables to a much higher standard, being more flexible and lighter and offering better protection in seawater with better insulation. Glass, Elliott became the main contender for the work, but with the improvements came an increase in projected costs, to £700,000, but they were prepared to negotiate.

When laying the initial transatlantic cable, due to the amount of cable required, two ships had been used, each starting from different sides of the ocean, to meet in mid-Atlantic to splice the cable together. However, by then, in 1864, one ship large enough to take the 2,500 miles of cable was available – the SS Great Eastern (incidentally 'SS' stands for 'Screw Steamer', rather than the 'Steam Ship' of popular misconception, with 'RMS' representing Royal Mail Ship and 'HMS', Her or His Majesty's Ship). The 18,000 ton ship, later to be renamed the SS Leviathan, was built in 1858 by Isambard Kingdom Brunel. It was 700 feet long and 85 feet wide, with 60-foot paddle wheels, five funnels and six masts, and was ideal for the task. It was capable of carrying

(The SS Great Eastern in all its splendour)

4,000 passengers and had the capacity to sail from England to Australia without refuelling en route, but had not proven financially viable and was currently lying idle. Glass, Elliott negotiated a deal with the owners, The Great Eastern Steamship Company, for it to start a new life as a cable-laying ship.

But the problem still remained as to how to find the extra capital required for the project, upwards of £300,000. The answer came from John Pender, as a director of the Atlantic Telegraph Company, who suggested the amalgamation of Glass, Elliott and the Gutta Percha Company under the new title of The Telegraph Construction and Maintenance Company Limited (Telcon). The company was duly registered in April 1864 with himself as Chairman and Richard Glass as Managing Director.

It had a capital of £1 million and it quickly confirmed the contract with the Great Eastern Company, whose managing director, Daniel Gooch, joined the Telcon board. In May, Telcon was contracted to make and lay the cable for £837,140 - £300,000 being paid in cash with the remainder in shares, an arguably somewhat risky investment.

And risky it proved. On 18th July 1864 fully laden with 25,000 tons of cable, the *SS Great Eastern* was duly seen off from Sheerness on the Thames estuary to Valentia on the west coast of Ireland with all due pomp and ceremony and the good wishes of Albert, Prince of Wales, the heir to the British throne. Under the command of Captain James Anderson she sailed from Valentia on 23rd July paying out cable as she sailed. The following day after only 84 miles the line went dead, the reason initially blamed on sabotage. The project was immediately abandoned and John Pender had to try to pick up the pieces. The Atlantic Telegraph Company threatened to sue Telcon, both companies of which Pender was a director. To his credit he certainly 'put his money where his mouth was' and offered to make and lay a new cable and to attempt to recover the lost section, and all for a total cost of £500,000.

The Atlantic Telegraph Company accepted the offer, perhaps because they had no other option, but the government ruled that they would have to form a new company to raise the money, so the Anglo-American Telegraph Company was born. As most of the original shareholders were by now too disillusioned to invest, Pender guaranteed the company with £250,000 of his and his wife, Emma Denison's money. His complete belief in the project allowed him to make such a gesture, no doubt against the advice of many friends and colleagues.

So on 13th July 1866 the *SS Great Eastern* set out again, in the third attempt to establish a submarine link between the two continents, completing its first run two weeks later on 27th July. On 9th August the ship continued its endeavours and on 2nd September it joined up the two ends of the cable and the link was finally made from Valentia to Heart's Content in Newfoundland, with their links at either end to Britain and the United States respectively. The ship, the wonder of its age, always struggled to be financially viable and after spending many years anchored off Milford Haven in Wales, it served as a floating music hall theatre with a grand dining saloon, before ultimately serving as a floating advertising hoarding, anchored off the city of Liverpool. It was eventually broken up for scrap in 1886. Perhaps the laying of the transatlantic cable had been its finest hour.

As a macabre and quite possibly apocryphal footnote to its chequered career, when being broken up for scrap, the skeleton of a man was found hidden between the walls of its double-skinned hull. It was said that he had been a pay clerk, the victim of robbery and murder by workmen during the construction of the ship. Ironically, if true, he had done something nobody else had managed – to be present on every sailing the ship made!

The Anglo-American Telegraph Company now operated the system, which was of immediate interest to the press, commercial interests and governments. The initial charge for a short message was the not inconsiderable sum of £20 and in December of that year a 4,000-word message sent from Washington to Paris, by the U.S. government, sent at 7 words per minute and taking ten hours, cost £2,000, an absolutely astronomical sum!

Other telegraph systems were springing up during this period, with Florida being linked to the West Indies and Argentina and Uruguay connected by the River Plate Telegraph Company, although the proposal by Western Union to connect the United States to Russia via the Bering Strait was abandoned once the transatlantic cable had been successfully laid. As the speed of development of telegraphic links increased, an International Bureau of Telegraph Administrations was founded in Paris to agree and standardise practices and procedures between major countries.

At this time the British government still with an eye on links from England to its Far East colonies, encouraged the Anglo-Mediterranean Telegraph Company which successfully completed a link from Malta to Alexandria in Egypt in October 1868. This was some 15 years after the failed attempt to span the Mediterranean by John Brett, but with the help of vast improvements to materials and technology over that period. This cable linked up with the line leading back northwards from Malta to Sicily and up through the length of Italy to the French border and onwards to England.

Meanwhile in 1868 on the domestic front, the Telegraph Purchase Bill enabled the Postmaster-General to buy out the shareholders in all the different electric telegraph companies in the United Kingdom whilst encouraging investment in overseas telegraph systems, whether using submarine cables or landlines and this was completed by 1870.

One investor keen to promote extending existing links and to create new ones to join Britain to India was John Pender, but for once he was beaten to the mark by the Anglo-Indian Telegraph Company, but when they went to the City of London for funding, they were unsuccessful and their short-lived company folded. Who would step into the breech, but John Pender of course with his British-Indian Submarine Telegraph Company founded in January 1869. Later that year concessions had been won to lay lines to Siam (now Thailand), Cambodia and French Indo-China (now Vietnam) with a plan to continue on to Hong Kong. He then founded a separate company, the Falmouth, Gibraltar and Malta Telegraph Company to complete the system of submarine cables between England and India. This new link commencing at Porthcurno, near Land's End in Cornwall, enabled the Secretary of State at Westminster to exercise direct control over events in India at a moment's notice, where previously the Viceroy of India had had to make urgent decisions himself on the spot, as previously a request to London for advice could take weeks or even months.

By 1872 Australia was linked to England from Port Darwin in the north of the country, to Porthcurno and with the continuing successful spread of telegraphic links to the countries of the Empire, there was considerable debate regarding a possible threat of the government taking over the assets of the Eastern Telegraph Company as it had proved to be not just financially viable but extremely profitable for its investors. Pender and the company had to live with such a possibility for many years.

Samuel Morse died in 1872 at the then 'ripe old' age of 80. He had lived to see his invention change the world in so many ways, bringing people closer together, revolutionising the worlds of business and government and bringing news from around the world to people's doorsteps on a daily basis.

He was much lauded around the world for his inventions, receiving every conceivable award and honour, dying a rich man and a much-respected

(*A prosperous looking John Pender, pictured in Vanity Fair in 1871 in its 'Men of the Day' series of caricatures by James Tissot*)

philanthropist, although his memories of the dire poverty he experienced in the early days as he followed his dream, stayed with him throughout his life.

(Samuel Morse, feted and decorated in old age)

In 1874 the cable link from England to Brazil was completed. It ran from Porthcurno to Lisbon, to Madeira, St Vincent, Cape Verde islands and on to

Recife in the north east of the country with further South American cable links laid throughout that decade, forming the basis of an important telegraphic link between Europe and South America.

In the same year, the Central Telegraph Office (CTO), the headquarters of the British inland telegram service, was transferred from its Telegraph Street premises to larger new premises in St. Martin's Le Grand, just a stone's throw from St. Paul's Cathedral. The move to the new CTO headquarters was necessary to cope with the increasing demand from both Victorian businesses and from private customers. The building was to take its part in the unfolding story of London's telegraphic history over the next 90 years, narrowly surviving two world wars.

In 1875 Pender announced the agreement with New Zealand for the construction and laying of a cable from Australia to New Zealand, spanning the 1,300 miles from Botany Bay near Sydney to Blind Bay at the northern end of New Zealand's South Island. The contract was fulfilled and the line was open for traffic in February 1876, two months ahead of schedule.

In 1877 John Pender celebrated his 30 years in submarine telegraphy with a knighthood, as the electric telegraph reached its fiftieth birthday.

In 1879, Pender continued his tireless pursuit of a worldwide submarine cable network, proposing the establishment of a link with South Africa running from Durban up the east African coast, which would join the existing Eastern Telegraph company system at Aden in The Yemen. The West African coast cable followed in 1886 and with each new cable came a new company to add to the Eastern Telegraph Company, eventually amalgamating into the Eastern and Associated Telegraph Companies.

In the early 1890s a challenge to the supremacy of the Eastern and Associated companies in Africa arose in the form of Cecil Rhodes who proposed an overland telegraphic link from Cape Town to Cairo, some 5,000 miles at a cost of between £400,000 and £500,000. If successful he intended to slash the cost per word of sending telegrams along the length of Africa to a quarter of what was then charged by the Eastern Group. As Rhodes' scheme seemed to depend mostly on his finding large quantities of gold 'beyond the *Limpopo*' it was always a little unlikely to succeed. The then General Manager of the Eastern Group, Sir James Anderson, who had in fact been the captain of the *SS Great Eastern* when it successfully laid the first transatlantic cable, expressed his lack of concern for the 'threat' from Rhodes when he pronounced that the company could look forward to being the 'carrying line for commercial traffic from the coast to the interior, since the natives, who do not wear clothes, are not in the habit of sending telegrams'.

(Sir John Pender – Victorian visionary)

In recognition of his achievements for services to the British Empire, for linking it and indeed most of the world, to England, Pender was created Knight Commander of St. Michael and St. George (K.C.M.G.) in 1888, and was further elevated to Knight Grand Cross of St. Michael and St. George (G.C.M.G.) in 1892. He died four years later in July 1896, aged 80, having over the years founded some 32 cable companies, and still at the helm of the 'Eastern' companies. Quite apart from his interest in submarine telegraphy, he was also involved with steam railways, notably as a director of the Isle of Man Steam Railway, having an engine named after him. He was also a director of the Chicago, St. Paul, Minneapolis & Omaha Railway in the U.S.A. If these interests were not enough to occupy him, he also was a collector of fine English paintings, notably by Turner, Landseer, Reynolds, Millais, Gainsborough and Canaletto.

He was one of the great Victorian achievers who never failed in his purpose to unite the world telegraphically and was always ready to risk his own capital in pursuit of his dream. Many who achieved far less are better remembered over a century later as household names. He was succeeded as chairman of the 'Eastern' companies by Lord Tweeddale, with his son John Denison-Pender as Managing-Director of the company.

As a lasting legacy to Sir John Pender, by 1898 the Eastern and Associated Telegraph Companies' network extended from Porthcurno, south to Carcavelos near Lisbon in Portugal and from there eastwards through the Mediterranean, the Suez Canal and the Red Sea across the Indian Ocean to India and onwards to Malaya, south to Australia and north east via Singapore and Hong Kong to Peking (now Beijing). The system had developed, not only following the spread of the British Empire, marked by large swathes of red on the map of the world, but also wherever substantial British interests lay.

The other branch from Carcavelos headed south to Madeira and St. Vincent before dividing, one branch encircling Africa and the other heading southwest to cover a large proportion of South America. Other links owned by the company connected Canada to the Caribbean and Florida via Bermuda. In addition to these lines of communication many countries had extensive overland links, mostly via a system of telegraph poles. In less than half a century the vision and ingenuity of pioneers such as Pender had seen amazing advances in technology.

The family interest in the Eastern and Associated companies was maintained by John Pender's son, John Denison-Pender, who had joined the board in 1881. He became Managing-Director in 1893, Deputy-Chairman in 1896 and finally Chairman in 1917. He was an important figure, much respected by staff and management alike as he piloted the company through the later stages of the First World War and into the post-war period which was to lead up to the Great Depression following the Wall Street Crash of 1929 – a time of great change for the company. Sadly, he was to succumb to pneumonia in March 1929, dying at the age of 73.

Radio Rears its 'Ugly' Head

By the turn of the twentieth century the cable companies were at the height of their powers, with a virtual monopoly on international telegraphy, but on the horizon a young Italian inventor and electrical engineer, Guglielmo Marconi was working on his fledgling wire-less transmission experiments. Marconi, born into nobility as Guglielmo Giovanni Maria Marconi in 1874, was the second son of Giuseppe Marconi, a wealthy landowner, and Annie Jameson, granddaughter of the founder of the Irish whisky distillers *Jameson and Sons*. He was educated both in Italy and England, and developed an early interest in science and electricity when studying in Italy under Augusto Righi, Professor of Physics at the University of Bologna.

When Marconi was 14, Heinrich Hertz had demonstrated the production and detection of electromagnetic radiation, or radio waves, which had first been postulated by James Clerk Maxwell in 1853. After Hertz's death in 1894, Marconi had access to the published accounts of his experiments and he then began to conduct his own experiments, sending and receiving signals over greater and greater distances. When he was ready to develop his wire-less telegraph machine he wrote to the Ministry of Posts and Telegraphs in Italy to ask for funding. He received no response, but it was later discovered that the minister concerned had written a note on Marconi's letter suggesting he be referred 'to the madhouse'.

Undeterred, Marconi asked for advice about leaving Italy to continue his experiments in England from a family friend who was Honorary Consul at the U.S. consulate in Bologna, and his friend subsequently gave him a letter of introduction to the Italian Ambassador in England. In 1896, aged 21, he arrived at Dover accompanied by his mother and was immediately put in touch with the Admiralty in London and subsequently with William Preece, the Chief Electrical Engineer of the Post Office. He was then given support to continue his experiments, sending messages over longer and longer distances in Britain.

In May 1897, after various false starts, he successfully demonstrated the transmission of wireless signals across the Bristol Channel to a select audience including Preece and Captain, later Lord, Baden-Powell, the founder of the Boy Scout movement. Later in December of that year he went on to set up the world's first permanent wireless station at the Royal Needles hotel in Alum Bay on the western tip of the Isle of Wight. The site was sufficiently remote from centres of population to avoid interference to the signals, especially that from tramways. Later, in July of that year, Marconi set up his Wireless Telegraph and Signal Company which subsequently became Marconi's Wireless Telegraph Company.

By 1898 his fame was spreading not least after demonstrating his system to Members of Parliament in London. He also attracted famous visitors to his Alum Bay wireless station, including Lord Kelvin, the eminent Irish-born physicist, who was initially unimpressed, although he did insist on paying one shilling each for messages he sent, thereby paying for the first commercial radio-telegrams. Two other 'celebrities', both local residents keen to take an interest in his work were Alfred, Lord Tennyson, the poet Laureate, who was rather more impressed than Kelvin, and Queen Victoria, who in her later years spent much of her time at Osborne House, her Isle of Wight retreat. She requested that a wireless station be installed at Osborne to enable her to receive daily reports about the Prince of Wales, the future King Edward VII, who was convalescing after fracturing a knee cap, on the royal yacht *Osborne*, moored off Cowes in the north of the island.

Marconi famously 'bridged' the English Channel in March 1899, a distance between stations of 32 miles and following this success he travelled to the United States to continue with his experiments. In November of that year, after his assistants had set up wireless equipment on the *SS St. Paul*, it became the first ocean liner to announce its imminent arrival at port from 66 nautical miles off the coast of England. It was not the first ship to be fitted with wireless facilities as the East Goodwin lightship, had been exchanging messages the previous year with the North Foreland lighthouse on the eastern tip of Northern Kent.

In 1901, Marconi set out on his most ambitious venture yet - to span the Atlantic with radio waves. His luck was out when in September of that year a tremendous storm brought down the large array of 200-foot masts at his Poldhu station on the Cornish cliff tops of the Lizard Peninsula. Undaunted, he quickly organised a team under his long time assistant George Kemp, to clear the debris and to erect a temporary replacement system – all within a week. The station was barely up and running when fate dealt him another cruel blow, when in November another great storm, across the Atlantic brought down the array of masts serving his planned Cape Cod station in Massachusetts.

Still hoping to rescue his plan, he set sail for Newfoundland later in the month with Kemp and his other assistant P. W. Paget. Once there his only hope

(Guglielmo Giovanni Maria Marconi in his 20s)

of receiving that first transatlantic signal was to keep his aerial wire aloft by means of a balloon or a kite. Thus, using a simple receiver and a kite borne antenna, he received the first historic trans-Atlantic radio signal, sent from Poldhu to Signal Hill at St. John's, Newfoundland.

At the time of the announcement of his spectacular feat many people were sceptical of his claims as they were not at the time independently verified. Some of the best scientific brains of the day had declared the attempt impossible and foolhardy and indeed his daylight transmission across the whole width of the Atlantic was later realised to be at the worst period for radio reception due to atmospheric conditions. Marconi however, sensitive to the criticism, arranged a further test and early the following year he sailed west again from Great Britain, receiving signals as he went on a daily basis, from his Poldhu station.

The signals confirmed that medium and long wave transmissions during each day travelled, were generally limited to hundreds, rather than thousands of miles but did travel much further at night, and by the end of the year the first successful radio signal was sent from west to east from Nova Scotia to Poldhu.

He had been forced to relocate his experiments from Newfoundland to Nova Scotia when the Anglo-American Telegraph Company, part of the Pender Group of companies and holders of a monopoly, banned his experiments there. In that same year the Eastern Telegraph Company built a radio antenna themselves with the help of their technical engineer John Jeffrey, at Pedn- men-an-Mere which became known as Wireless Point, just to the west of Porthcurno - specifically to spy on Marconi's transmissions from Poldhu, some 17 miles away on the Lizard Peninsula. The company mistakenly concluded that Marconi's efforts would not constitute a threat to their supremacy over world telegraphy, but they could hardy have been more wrong.

Marconi's Poldhu Station continued to function as a working wireless and research station until 1933 and was demolished in 1937. His other nearby building, the Lizard Wireless Telegraph Station still stands today, and was restored by *The National Trust* in 2001 to celebrate the centenary of Marconi spanning the Atlantic. It looks much as it did over a century ago. The station is currently run as a museum by members of *The Poldhu Amateur Radio Club* (GB2GM), and is open to the public from March each year. (www.lizardwireless.org)

Many other eminent Victorian scientists had also experimented with wireless waves and electro-magnetism, not least Sir Henry Jackson who, knowing nothing of Marconi's early work had been successfully sending wireless signals over some distance, but unfortunately at the time of his experiments his work was hidden in confidential military reports and not publicly known for many years. Sir William Preece, summing up Marconi's achievements, was quoted as saying "They all knew the egg, but Marconi showed them how to stand it on end".

Commercial wireless telegraphy services duly commenced in October 1907 between Clifden in Galway in Ireland and Glace Bay in Nova Scotia in Canada. If Marconi's place in history had not already been cemented, being jointly awarded the *Nobel Prize in Physics* in 1909 with Karl Ferdinand Braun (1850-1918), for their work in developing wireless telegraphy, was the recognition he deserved from the establishment. German-born Braun had created the first cathode-ray tube in 1897 and it was subsequently to become the corner stone of full electronic television.

Another milestone in the use of wireless communications was reached when in 1910 the first message was sent from an aeroplane in flight to a ground station, on Salisbury Plain in Wiltshire, a small step which would lead eventually to today's sophisticated global network connecting aircraft with airports. The other milestone in aviation achieved just one year earlier was the first flight across the English Channel from France to England by Louis Blériot, who in doing so won the not insubstantial sum of £1,000 in prize money from the *Daily Mail* newspaper.

April 1912 brought the terrible *Titanic* disaster when more than 700 passengers and crew were saved with the help of wireless distress messages from the ship, but there was an earlier drama which took place off the eastern United States in January 1909 which history seems to have forgotten about. A collision between the *RMS Republic* and the liner the *SS Florida* left the *Republic* in danger of sinking. Wireless operator Jack Binns of the *Republic* heroically stayed at his post for 18 hours aboard the sinking ship, sending out repeated SOS messages and as a result all 1500 passengers and crew were saved through a US coastguard station picking up the calls and various vessels quickly rushed to the scene to help with the rescue. His heroism and the wonder of the new technology captured the public's attention and the importance of the Marconi wireless telegram was firmly established. Marconi was subsequently to offer Binns the prestigious position of wireless operator on the *White Star Line*'s newest ship – the *Titanic*, but as Binns was recently engaged to his American sweetheart, she persuaded him to give up the sea and he declined Marconi's offer, and a day before the *Titanic* sank he had begun work as a reporter for a New York newspaper, reporting on one of the century's biggest stories which, ironically, he had been part of. Eventually, from 1919, all British passenger ships and cargo ships of 1,600 tons upwards were legally bound to have a wireless telegraphy system fitted.

Marconi's efforts were to go from strength to strength especially after he had secretly developed his *Short-wave Beam Wireless System,* which in the long term proved extremely successful, to the extent that by the 1920s it began to threaten the supremacy of the Eastern Telegraph Company in certain areas. In addition, the Post Office by arrangement with the Marconi Company operated beam wireless services from its Rugby wireless station from 1927. These connected London with Australia, Canada, South Africa and India.

Other radio pioneers deserve recognition, notably Oliver Heaviside and Arthur Kennelly who independently proposed the existence of a layer of ionised gas in what is now known as the ionosphere, which reflected medium wave radio transmissions back to earth, enabling transmission beyond the horizon, which explained Marconi's success in transmitting beyond the line of sight. The existence of what is generally known as the Heaviside Layer was not proven until 1924 by Edward V. Appleton (1892–1965) who calculated the height of the ionosphere commencing at 56 miles above the earth. Appleton and New Zealander, Miles Barnett (1901–1979) had another atmospheric layer, the Appleton-Barnett Layer, which reflected high frequency radio signals, named in their honour. Appleton was also awarded the *Nobel Prize in Physics*, in 1947.

It was known from early days that telegraphic transmission, whether by cable or wireless could be strongly affected by solar activity when at the height of the 11-year cycle, solar flares potentially produced Coronal Mass Ejections (CMEs). If the earth is in the firing line of a CME it can result in strong displays of the Northern and Southern Lights (Aurora Borealis and Aurora Australis) and can also damage orbiting satellites and cause power outages on a grand scale. In perhaps the most violent CME event in recent history, in May 1921, the Northern Lights were visible as far south as Texas in the southern United States and telegraphic services suffered catastrophic breakdowns, mostly due to blown fuses and damaged equipment, and undersea cables also suffered significant damage due to the severity of the event.

Another possible cause of disruption was discovered in November 1929 when an underwater earthquake in mid Atlantic knocked nine transatlantic cables out of action for a while. But on balance the general reliability of cables over wireless and satellite communication has not been seriously challenged and satellites account for only some 30% of global communications and without the submarine fibre-optic cable network the Internet would not operate successfully.

Fierce competition between the two systems continued through the 1920s, and it was getting all rather confusing for the Man in the Street, when one could send a telegram *Via Imperial Cable* or *Wireless,* a *Marconigram* by wireless or through the Post Office's Imperial Wireless *Via Empiradio* system, but pressure was rising to unite the companies under one banner into what eventually was to become Cable and Wireless Ltd.

Chapter Two

Electra House(s) – The Early Days

Electra House, Moorgate

The original Electra House, situated at 84 Moorgate, EC2 in the City of London, was designed in 1900 by Belcher & Joass, and it opened in 1902 to become the headquarters of the Eastern and Associated Submarine Telegraph Companies, and to provide accommodation for 850 staff. It was to preside over the eventual amalgamation of the Eastern and Marconi companies into becoming Cable & Wireless Ltd., and it was used as London Station until 1941 in conjunction with the adjoining Tower Chambers. Tower Chambers had been built in 1879 on the site of a Presbyterian chapel, and looking further back into history, was on the site of the Old Bethlehem Hospital, from where we get the word 'Bedlam', which had been demolished in 1814.

The Moor Gate itself had been constructed in medieval times as a postern, or subsidiary gate in the old London Wall, which was built by the Romans around 200 A.D. The gate was the work of City of London Mayor Thomas Falconer, who had occupied that prestigious position in the reign of Henry V (1387–1422). At that time Londoners wishing to access Moor Fields, just outside the city wall, for wild fowling or more importantly archery practice, would have to go the long way round via either Bishopsgate or Cripplegate. The Moor Gate was rebuilt in 1672 after the Great Fire of London and demolished in 1761, the stones being used to strengthen the piers on the Old London Bridge. This bridge in turn was replaced by a 19th century structure, later to take up residence at Lake Havasu in Arizona in the 1960s.

The word 'Electra' deriving from *'Elektron'*, the Greek for amber, was a suitably progressive name for the headquarters building of a telegraph company at the cutting edge of early 20th century technology. Appropriately, perhaps the best-known character of that name in Greek mythology was Electra, the daughter of Clytemnestra and Agamemnon, reflecting back to the laying of the first transatlantic cable in the 1850s, when the *SS Agamemnon* and the *USS Niagara* had assisted in the unsuccessful attempt to join the two continents. The name was to have further resonance later in the telecommunications story when Marconi named his steam yacht Elettra in 1919, and his daughter Maria Elettra when she was born in 1930.

Prior to the construction of the new headquarters, the 'Eastern' group of telegraph companies had been based, since 1885, at Winchester House, 50, Old Broad Street (demolished 1965) in the City of London, together with premises at number 66, almost opposite, until the company's expansion necessitated the move to larger premises.

(Electra House, Moorgate, 1902)

Electra House, built predominantly from Portland Stone, with a ground floor of Cornish granite, still stands proudly on its Moorgate site, with a broad frontage between London Wall and West Street, which is now incorporated into an approach road to Finsbury Circus. It is described as 'an iconic Grade II listed building' and it boasts many fine architectural features, especially those of its grand façade and main entrance. The large arched portal supports two 'spandrels' with sculptures by George Frampton depicting one figure on the left transmitting a message to a second figure on the right, whilst the keystone at the top of the arch sports a shield portraying Prometheus, the Greek titan who brought fire to mankind.

The building comprises a basement and six storeys above, with its rooftop surmounted by an impressive dome, crowned by bronzes of young Atlases supporting a large armillary sphere and zodiacal band placed diagonally around it, 141 feet above the pavement, the work of F. W. Pomeroy.

(Crowning Glory, Electra House, Moorgate)

There are also several sculpted panels decorating the face of the building including more allegorical figures representing India, China, Japan and Egypt. These and those decorating the foyer are by Pomeroy, Alfred Drury, George Frampton and William Goscombe John, all of whom were important artists working at the turn of the 20th century. Above the main entrance is a large semi-circular stained glass work depicting an 'allegorical figure seated on the earth's Globe, with allegorical rays of electrical energy streaming from her', against a background of stars. At the bottom of the central panel, a lighthouse and a 'galleon' under full sail, are depicted. This is seen in its best light on a sunny day from within the foyer of the building and looking outwards.

(Dramatic 'demi-lune' stained glass design, Electra House, Moorgate)

Much renovation and redecoration work has been done to the building in recent years to bring it back to its former glory. It had been hoped that the ceiling of the foyer would reveal paintings of classical figures, the work of George Murray, hidden under layers of whitewash, but it now appears that despite the survival of a full colour artist's sketch of the artwork, the work had probably never been implemented.

At the time of the building's construction, the Eastern and Associated companies owned over 100,000 nautical miles of submarine cables (one nautical mile = 1.151 miles) and nearly 6,000 miles of overhead lines, with 227 cable stations dotted around the world, 93 in Europe, 27 in Asia, 49 in Africa, 49 in South America and 9 in Australia and New Zealand, with the total staff both home and abroad numbering 3,200. Stations in the United States had not been set up, as Western Union and other companies had the market 'sewn up' with telegraph offices in virtually every town and city. Indeed Western Union alone had opened more than 21,000 telegraph offices by the end of the 19th century. But, with substantial links from the Eastern companies in London to the continental United States, there would be good co-operation and a steady and healthy flow of telegraphic traffic between the networks.

In the early days Electra House housed the 'A' and 'B' rooms of the company training school in the basement. Here aspiring engineers and operators would be instructed in the use of cable keys, vibrator recorders, hand perforators, pendulum-clockwork transmitters and other long-forgotten items of vital equipment from the early days of the 20th century. A new London training school was subsequently established at Shepherd's Walk, Hampstead, in north London, which opened in January 1920 with facilities for training 200 new recruits at a time. With the expansion of telegraphic services after the First World War, this figure rose to 350 by 1922. Apart from a hiatus following the Great Depression of the 1930s, it continued as the company training school until the Second World War, when the building was requisitioned by the General Post Office for use as a postal sorting office.

The basement of the Moorgate building also accommodated two fire-proof rooms, various vaults, and a carpenter's shop, with sundry other rooms occupied by the London Joint Stock Bank Limited, which also rented the corresponding space on the floor above at street level.

The main entrance on the ground floor led through the foyer to a lift and stairs, with the traffic department of the Eastern Telegraph Company being to one side, and, in the early days, a public counter plus various vacant rooms, which in due course were to be occupied as the company expanded. A small secondary private lift, discreetly tucked away, gave access for the directors to their quarters.

The flooring of the main entrance and all the corridors was laid in Sicilian and black marble squares of a unique design and in addition the marble columns flanking the main entrance were made from Swiss Cippolino, or Onion Stone, and rested on marble bases and were topped with bronze capitols. The columns, which are monoliths, are over 11ft. long. Sadly, the original bronze gates, which once adorned the main entrance, have long since left the premises, apparently disappearing without trace.

From the first floor upwards three voids, clad in white glazed bricks, were incorporated into the building, reducing the floor space available, but bringing much needed daylight to the inner rooms of the building. The first floor was initially vacant, awaiting tenants, with the company proper occupying the building from the second to the fifth floors.

Directors and the administration filled the second and third floors with the Chairman, Vice-Chairman and directors housed on the former and the General Manager and his staff on the latter. Evidently there were many board meetings anticipated, as two boardrooms were built, one on each floor, with that on the third floor seeming to be the one of choice for meetings, although the one on the second floor housed the portrait in oils of Sir John Pender. The circuits of the Eastern and Associated telegraph companies primarily occupied the fourth and fifth floors, with a doctor's 'surgery' squeezed in a corner of the fourth. These associated companies included the Western, the African Direct, the London-Platino Brazilian, the River Plate and the West Coast of America. The names reflected the many companies set up years earlier by Sir John Pender, each time he instituted a new cable link.

The sixth floor housed various service areas, a laboratory for the Electrical Department and a flat for the housekeeper. All in all, there were exactly 100 rooms in the building.

It goes without saying that the building was fitted with electric lighting throughout, as electrical power was at the very heart of its *raison d'etre* and no expense was spared in the state-of-the-art technical outfitting of the building. An extensive intercom system was also installed, along with external telephone lines to contact subscribers. Another important communications system used by the company was that of the pneumatic tube, which used compressed air to propel a carrier holding telegrams or other messages along the tube. Such a system connected Electra House with the Associated Companies station at 11, Old Broad Street. The tube was laid under the road surface and it took 'about 53 seconds' for a carrier tube to go between offices, a considerable saving of time and expense over sending a messenger that distance. Pneumatic tube systems would be in use in most telegraph offices for many years to come.

The Electra House building sits immediately adjacent to the tunnel built for the new London Crossrail project and the work has severely affected the eastern end of the building, which has required a considerable amount of shoring up. Any movement in the building and damage caused to it is being closely monitored and it could take years to resolve the problems caused.

The London Crossrail project, subsequently renamed the Elizabeth Line in honour of Queen Elizabeth II, is one of Europe's largest railway and infrastructure schemes, entailing 73 miles of track and incorporating 26 miles of new tunnels under London. It stretches from east to west, linking branches from north and south of the Thames in Essex and Kent respectively, then through central London extending westwards to link with Heathrow Airport. It then continues westwards to Reading in Berkshire where it connects to rail services to the southwest. The project also features further in the story of London telegraph offices, as it has necessitated the demolition of Cardinal House near Smithfield, another major telegraph station, which began operations in the 1960s.

The First World War

With the outbreak of the First World War, telegraphic communication took on a new importance, with the corresponding increase in government and civilian traffic. Thus on 5th August 1914 the decision was taken by the British government to cut all accessible German undersea cables, which was not difficult as five of the eleven were laid east to west along the English Channel which was then very much under British control. The cable ship *CS Alert*, anchored off the German coast, discreetly lowered its grappling irons under cover of darkness to raise and cut the cables. The five severed links had been connected to Brest on the Atlantic coast of France, to Vigo in Spain, to Tenerife in the Canary Islands, with two cables stretching across the Atlantic Ocean to the U.S.A. via the Azores.

One of these latter cables was diverted three years later into Mousehole, the picturesque Cornish fishing village, situated some eight miles from Porthcurno, and just across Mount's Bay from the Lizard peninsula, whilst at the other end, the Fayal to New York link was diverted to Halifax, Nova Scotia for British government use. The remaining six cables were all connected to England, and these were officially 'interrupted' on the outbreak of hostilities. Any links the Germans tried to use across the Mediterranean were also in British hands.

This left the Germans' only foreign telegraphic links via landline to their ally Austria, or to neutral countries, which would not accept messages in code. Alternatively they could send messages by radio, which could be intercepted and possibly decoded by the British. To further thwart the enemy, the allies had destroyed most of the German overseas wireless stations. What the Germans were not to know as the war progressed, was that the allies would capture a secret naval communication code book as well as a chest containing other codes, jettisoned by a sinking enemy destroyer, giving the allies a distinct edge, to be echoed by an even greater advantage, by the cracking of the German 'Enigma' codes, during the Second World War.

At that time the Germans did attempt to establish radio links with the U.S.A., which was still a neutral country, but with poor results due to excessive 'static'. This possibility would be short-lived once the allies had intercepted the infamous 'Zimmerman' telegram of 16th January 1917, sent by the German foreign minister Arthur Zimmerman to the German ambassador in Mexico, Heinrich von Eckhardt, urging him to persuade President Carranza to attack the U.S.A. in exchange for the 'return' of Texas, New Mexico and Arizona, once Germany had won the war. The message was subtly leaked in Washington, D.C. with the resultant predictable public outcry and rise in anti-German sentiment, after which President Woodrow Wilson had the support of the public to enter the war on the side of the allies.

It was during the 1914-18 war that women telegraph operators were first introduced by the Eastern Group, as a great shortage of men resulted from a national recruitment drive encouraging them to enlist in the armed forces. Telegraph operators skilled in Morse working, would have been a highly valued commodity in the forces at that time.

By 1923 a new figure emerged who would play an important role in the development of post-war telecommunications - Anglo-Canadian Colin Campbell Stuart who was the Canadian government representative of the Pacific Cable Board. This ambitious cable had been laid in 1902 to link Canada with Australia and New Zealand and was jointly owned by the British and Canadian governments. At that time it included the longest stretch of cable in the world, 3467 miles, stretching from Bamfield in Western Canada to Fanning Island (now known as Tabuaeran) in the middle of the Pacific Ocean. During the 1920s Campbell Stuart had become increasingly concerned with the intense competition between the wireless and cable companies and bearing in mind the vital need to protect and regulate communication services, especially in time of war, he recommended that the question should be considered at an Imperial Conference.

As a measure of the worldwide domination of the Eastern company's cable system at that time, King George V when opening the 1924 British Empire Exhibition at Wembley, sent a telegram to himself which travelled around the world and back again in one minute and twenty seconds!

Thus an Imperial Wireless and Cable Conference was set up in London in January 1928 with Campbell Stuart representing the Canadian government. At the same time Sir William Plender representing the Eastern Associated Companies and Sir Gilbert Garnsley of the Marconi Wireless Telegraph Company 'compiled a joint report for submission to their respective boards as to a possible arrangement in the joint interests of the respective companies'. The conference recommended the setting up of an Imperial Communications Committee, which eventually was to lead to the formation of the Cables and Wireless Company, of which Campbell Stuart became the first chairman. Not all members of the Marconi Company were happy with the arrangement, some feeling they had not secured a fair deal, but any dissenting voices were in the minority. In addition, their position was not strengthened by talk in the City of the 'reckless mismanagement' of the Marconi Company.

Despite all the meetings and negotiations taking place, progress in refining the cable system continued apace, embracing new technology and fresh ideas, and in January 1929 new ground was broken when a direct link between London and Singapore, a distance of some 7,000 miles, was established for the first time. It used automatic 'regenerators' spaced at intervals along the line, obviating the need for relaying stations to play any part in sending on messages.

With the merger of the Eastern and Associated Telegraph Companies (Eastern, Western and Eastern Extension) with Marconi's Wireless Telegraph Company in 1929, following the passing of the *Telegraph Act of 1928*, Marconi's operating circuits were transferred from his Radio House headquarters at 2-12 Wilson Street, which at the time housed the Marconi Company's main telegraph office with a counter office for filing messages, bearing the telephone number BIShopsgate 6565. The company's 'Telegraph School' was housed in the basement of the building. The Wilson Street building (currently the home of *'Bangers Bar & Grill'*), is just a few hundred yards away from the Electra House, Moorgate building. These services were later to be joined by the intercontinental telegram services, Imperial cables and the *'Empiradio'* Beam radio circuits, acquired from the Post Office. Whilst all the operating circuits were now sited under the one roof, the administrative staffs were still spread around various other Central London buildings.

The new joint-board, or 'Court of Directors' met for the first time in the third-floor boardroom on 8th April of that year, taking its new name to emulate that of the directors of the Bank of England. The new Eastern/Marconi 'Court' consisted of 22 members, including Lord Inverleith, John Cuthbert Denison-Pender, who had become joint-Managing Director of the Eastern Company in 1925, and Marconi, still keen to take an active part in the company he had helped create.

In its heyday in the 1930s, the Moorgate building housed hundreds of operating staff spread over several floors whilst at the adjacent Tower Chambers on the corner of Moorgate and London Wall there was a telegram acceptance counter where, under the large imposing capital letters 'CABLE AND WIRELESS', with a diagonal italic flourish of *'Via Imperial'* below, City businesses could deliver their messages, or the public could drop in to write out their telegrams for onward transmission overseas *'Via Imperial'* (*Via*

(Interior of Board Room, Electra House, Moorgate)

Marconigram, Via Eastern, and other route designations having been dropped in favour of this term in the early 1930s).

Alternatively customers could send a telegram by telephoning METropolitan 6644, with 6666 being used for customers' enquiries. These calls were dealt with by the predominantly female Telephone Room staff in Electra House. At the same time, especially during weekday business hours, there was a constant stream of received messages destined for City customers, all neatly gummed down on the relevant message forms and folded into a distinctive envelope, ready for one of the company's 450-strong corps of messenger boys to deliver it promptly to a local office. This army of messengers was spread around Electra House and various City branch offices and rarely would have congregated *en masse*, although one such occasion in June 1939 was a visit to the Aldershot Military Tattoo, which saw 300 uniformed lads gather outside Tower Chambers to await a string of double-decker buses to transport them on an exciting day's outing.

(Uniformed messengers posing in front of Tower Chambers)

In those pre-war days messenger boys were recruited directly from school aged 14, the then legal minimum leaving age. They worked 48 hours per week and were paid 14 shillings a week. Despite the lowly wage and status they were encouraged to progress within the company and depending on ambition and aptitude could rise in time to positions of authority as many did.

Popular with the staff over the years were the *Moorgate* and the *Globe*, two pubs situated virtually opposite Electra House. Still surviving, they are sited side by side at 83 and 85 Moorgate, conveniently 'bracketing' Electra House at number 84. In recent years the appropriately named *Globe* has been absorbed into the *Moorgate* and renamed the *Keats at the Globe*, the name referring to the 'fact' that John Keats, the poet, was born there in 1795, his father then running the livery stables at the pub, which at that time was named the 'Swan and Hoop'. Keats was subsequently baptised at nearby St. Botolph's church in Bishopsgate, which will have further resonance later in the story. Also, well frequented by staff was the nearby London Wall Restaurant, popularly known in those days as the 'Electra House Annex'.

Electra House, Victoria Embankment

Meanwhile, in 1929, the site for the new Electra House was purchased at Temple Place (formerly The Approach), Victoria Embankment, along with the red brick Victorian Arundel House and its lesser adjunct, FitzAlan House, adjoining it to the west, and just outside the boundary of the square mile of the City of London. Until mid-Victorian times the site would have directly overlooked the Thames with the river virtually lapping at its feet, but once the Victoria Embankment was constructed to control the river, it avoided periodic flooding and helped to ease traffic congestion in the nearby Strand which since medieval times had been the main route between the City of London and Westminster, the home of parliament and the sovereign. As part of the work, some 80 yards of the original foreshore was recovered, being part of the 37 acres of the land reclaimed which allowed for the construction of the current Victoria Embankment roadway and for what was to become Temple Gardens.

The scheme also formed an important part of the move to rid London of 'The Great Stink', caused by poor facilities for sewage disposal, which since Roman times had been allowed to run freely into the Thames. Prior to reclaiming the land and narrowing the river, there were extensive 'mud flats' primarily composed of raw sewage, which had traditionally drained into the river to be washed down stream on an out-going tide and brought back on the in-coming one. At low tide these deposits had to be treated with quantities of chalk, chloride of lime and carbolic acid. Along with the District Line underground tunnel sunk at the same time, a main sewer carrying waste from west to east was also constructed. The work was funded from a duty on coal being brought to the Capital, which was levied by the City of London Corporation. The idea of building an embankment had first been mooted by Sir Christopher Wren after the Great Fire of London in 1666, but the first stone was not to be laid until 1862, with the project being completed in 1870 and officially opened by Queen Victoria. The work, at a cost of £2 million, was the brainchild of Sir Joseph Bazalgette, the man credited with the extensive construction of London's sewer system a few years earlier.

The new Electra House, along with the adjoining Arundel House, was bordered by Arundel Street and Water Lane to the west and Milford Lane to the east, with the curiously named Tweezer's Alley to the north. The origin of this name is obscure, but it appears it might relate to a blacksmiths business established there hundreds of years ago, one which manufactured oversize

(An 1869 view, left to right, from Somerset House to the Middle Temple with Arundel Street right of centre)

tweezers. Another possibility is that it could be etymologically related to the word 'twitten', an 'alleyway or narrow passage between two walls'.

The alley was not without its own history. It was apparently the home for the blacksmiths and adjacent stables used by the London General Omnibus Company, which ran horse-drawn buses from mid-Victorian times until 1911, by which time the company switched to motorised omnibuses. The forge and stables were eventually taken over by W. H. Smith and Co. and as late as the 1920s they were still using horse-drawn vehicles, no doubt to facilitate the delivery of newspapers, magazines and books to their central London shops and kiosks, notably sited in all the major railway stations. Little currently remains of Tweezer's Alley due to the intensive redevelopment of the area in recent times, but a street name plate for the alley can still be found on the north side of Globe House, which replaced Electra House.

Arundel House was built by the Duke of Norfolk in 1884, and until 1928, it had been used by the Arundel Hotel, whose main building, a Victorian Gothic structure, offering 100 bedrooms, was situated on the corner, just across Arundel Street. In later years Arundel House was to provide offices for solicitors including William Rollo, the father-in-law of the actor David Niven, who was a familiar visitor in his RAF uniform during World War II. Sadly Niven's wife 'Primmie' (Primula Rollo) was to die in a tragic accident at the home of the actor Tyrone Power, in 1946, aged 28.

From 1941 onwards the firm of solicitors moved upstairs, and the building was to provide a telegram acceptance counter on the ground floor, with internal access to Electra House and its overseas circuits.

In more recent times, in the 1990s, Arundel House has been occupied by Marvel Comics with their latter-day superheroes such as Spider-Man and the Incredible Hulk. Its current occupants are the IISS (International Institute for Strategic Studies) who have occupied the building since late 1997. Interestingly, at the turn of the 21st century, it was decided to add another floor to the building, not an easy task with a structure described as 'Tudor Revival', crowned by a turreted roof and tall ornate chimneys. The top storey and roof were duly removed and a new matching fifth floor was 'inserted', and the roof with all its idiosyncrasies, including replacement chimney pots, was expertly re-instated – from street level one can hardly see the join!

The original Arundel House, situated south of the Strand on one side of Milford Lane, on land sloping down to moorings and wharfs on the Thames, was built in the 13th century as a grand residence for the Bishop of Bath and

(Arundel House, before (late 1990s), and after the addition of an extra storey in 2001)

Wells. After Henry VIII's Reformation in 1537 it was confiscated and eventually, in 1549, found its way into the possession of Henry FitzAlan, 12th Earl of Arundel, for a mere £40! It had a long and sometimes notorious history as a grand residence and also as an art gallery, and it was demolished in 1682. On the other side of Milford Lane was Essex House, originally named Leicester House when it was built in the 1570s. It was renamed Essex House when Robert Devereux, the 2nd Duke of Essex, his step-son, inherited the building in 1588, the year of the Spanish Armada. Essex, famously close to Queen Elizabeth I, was executed at the Tower of London in 1601 after leading a failed revolt against his sovereign. The main part of the house was demolished in the 1670s, with Essex Street being built on part of the site.

The proposed site for the new Electra House was on land that was once occupied by extensive gardens belonging to the original medieval Arundel House. In the days prior to the creation of the Victoria Embankment, there were just two accesses to the Thames in the immediate area, Milford Lane to the east and Strand Bridge Lane to the west, which ran down to the river next to Somerset House.

After the Victoria Embankment came into being there was a growth of grand Victorian Gothic buildings occupying the river side and the future site of

Electra House was occupied from the early 1870s by the London School Boards building. With its imposing façade it was no exception, and at the end of its life had been in use as offices for the London County Council Tramways Department. It was duly demolished in 1929 to make way for the new building provisionally to be named 'Temple House', it being situated close to The Temple, the traditional home to generations of lawyers, and opposite to Temple Underground station.

Designed by Sir Herbert Baker in the Classical Revival style, Electra House was completed three years later in 1932. Built by Trollope and Colls Ltd. of Portland stone on a polished granite base, it occupied a site measuring 36,250 square feet, with a floor area of approximately 183,570 square feet extending across its 10 floors. It measured 138 feet 6 inches in height from basement to roof and boasted five staircases plus six passenger-lifts that travelled at 400 feet per minute and were capable of carrying up to 12 persons.

(Electra House, Victoria Embankment - Artist's impression)

(Main entrance with steps, statuary and symbolism)

Its imposing main entrance doors were 'in bronze, with red painted teak inner doors; the main entrance hall extending upwards through two floors, lined with polished Ancaster stone.' Ancaster stone is a form of limestone quarried in Lincolnshire and famously used on such historic buildings as Norwich Cathedral and St. John's College, Cambridge, not forgetting its use for sculptures by Henry Moore and Barbara Hepworth. Above the 30 foot semi-circular entrance archway and below a small balcony, was an apt and stylish sculpture featuring a strong right hand clasping a stylised lightning bolt and a length of cable, all surrounded by a circle of links of a chain.

(Interior of foyer with World War I memorial to the fallen)

The floor of the entrance hall featured a round compass design, accentuating North and South, whilst the entrance steps were flanked by two small rooms, the House Superintendent's office on the left and a waiting room on the right, with access to both from the entrance hall. Crossing the foyer one was confronted by two large glass doors which opened on to what was to become a telegram acceptance counter in the Local Room on the upper ground floor. Early in World War II this access was closed off and the acceptance counter in neighbouring Arundel House was set up.

The building was designed to be as self-sufficient as possible bearing in mind the need for an uninterrupted service, and it housed its own powerful electricity generators plus a water tank with a capacity of 85,000 gallons. The tank was connected to a water softening process in the basement, and fed by two artesian wells, which produced 3,500 gallons per hour. Water supply by artesian well was also later to be shared by the Falcon House area office in the City. In addition, practically every room in the building was joined via an automatic telephone system and every office was also fitted with a clock synchronized with a master clock situated on the lower ground floor. The front of the building was also fitted with floodlights to highlight its prominent position overlooking the Thames. This feature was quickly disconnected once war was declared against Germany in 1939.

A grand, prestigious building, with steel window frames throughout, it comprised a basement, lower and upper ground floors plus seven storeys sitting on top. Looking out to the south over Temple Gardens to the nearby Thames with the *RRS Discovery*, *HQS Wellington*, *HMS Chrysanthemum* and *HMS President* moored in the foreground, it was handsome to the eye from all angles and a fitting new headquarters for a major international company.

Plans had been announced previously, that as a result of the merger of the Eastern group and the Marconi Company, the London operations would be consolidated all under one roof at the new Victoria Embankment premises and that Electra House and Tower Chambers, Moorgate, along with Marconi House on The Strand, would all be 'disposed of' via their estate agent of choice, Knight, Frank and Rutley of Hanover Square. Marconi House had had its own special place in the history of communications. In 1922 the building had featured as the venue for Marconi's early collaboration with the fledgling BBC when on 11th May the first radio broadcast from Station 2LO took place. The first 'pre-announced' broadcast had taken place two years earlier on 15th June, 1920 when Dame Nellie Melba, the major diva and opera star of her day, sang live from Marconi's works at Chelmsford in Essex.

The timing of the new joint company's expansion plans was extremely unfortunate as the 1929 Wall Street Crash, and subsequent worldwide financial depression, made an immediate and serious impact on the company's finances. There had to be immediate and drastic savings on the company's £5,300,000 a year annual expenditure and by the end of 1929 the staff of 8,429 employees around the world had been reduced by 645, mostly through voluntary retirement, and over the next few years a further 1,500 were made redundant, saving the company some £370,000 a year. In addition the company's fleet of cable ships was reduced from 11 to 6 with the resultant loss of 40 'marine officers'. The directors of the company were equally to 'feel the pinch' as their numbers decreased from 22 to 14, with those remaining taking a voluntary 20% reduction in their directorship fees. However, it was not all 'doom and gloom' in the Court Room, as all the directors who resigned received a compensation payment of £10,500 – perhaps 20 times the average wage of the day, assuming one was lucky enough to have a job in those desperate times!

The need for such a dramatic reduction in staff numbers was of course partly due to the amalgamation of the cable and wireless companies, but whatever the reason, many loyal employees faced an uncertain future at a difficult time. It was a very sad and drawn out process as many long-time staff members who expected to be working for the company 'till retirement age', had to leave the company prematurely after receiving their D/N (D bar N) notices. You might think that D/N would stand for 'Dismissal Notice' but it simply related to the date and time of the message announcing the dismissals, 'D' representing the fourth day and 'N' standing for 1300 hours, using the 24-hour clock, with 'A' being 0100, etc, and 'J' being omitted. It can have been of little comfort to them to know that the directors of the company had taken substantial voluntary reductions to their fees.

Then, Lo and Behold! once completed in 1932, the directors of the company put the new Electra House building on the market for sale! A statement from the board claimed the decision was 'owing to the adverse effect of the world crisis on Imperial and International Communications Ltd., which has inevitably entailed a drastic readjustment of arrangements' – not the most straightforward of statements you might think. The decision was made after company 'receipts' had dropped by 9% in 1931, and it was taken in the light of the need to drastically cut costs, eventually leading to a major round of redundancies, with total global staff numbers, both operating and administrative, being reduced in a few years by 25% from around 12,000 to less than 9,000 personnel. The drop in profitability was not as bad as it might seem. When put into context, the main rival companies in America, Western Union and Commercial Cable saw their receipts for the same period falling by 16.7% and 19.4% respectively.

At the same time, Mr. John Cuthbert Denison-Pender as Chairman, made a dramatic appeal to the staff throughout the world to make a contribution towards the company for the remainder of the year by increasing their working hours by one hour per week on a *pro bono* basis, resulting in less overtime and Sunday duty being available. The response from the staff was reported as 'instantaneous and overwhelming', resulting in a saving to the company of up to £200,000 that year. The company received the full support for this measure from the Imperial and International Communications Staffs' Association, representing the employees, however although members were successfully balloted for their approval, there were many dissenting voices and all was not well subsequently within the Association, and it was to disband shortly afterwards.

Another event taking place in 1932, which perhaps passed almost unnoticed amongst all the fanfare of the opening of the new building and the fall-out from the Great Depression, following the Wall Street Crash of 1929, was the launching of the telex system whereby one subscriber could send messages by teleprinter over a network to another subscriber. This was followed in 1936 by the first operator-assisted continental service. The telex system was to come into its own in the post-war period, reaching its zenith in the 1970s.

An imposing sale brochure for Electra House was printed and circulated but due to the continuing effects of the Great Depression, there were no takers.

And then in early 1933, rumours began to spread, notably on the front page of the London *Evening News*, that the Victoria Embankment building would indeed be put to the use it was intended and was to become the company headquarters. Thus on 11th May, 1933, the new Electra House, sporting its distinctive telephone number TEMple Bar 1222, was officially opened by Mrs. John Cuthbert Denison-Pender, wife of the Chairman of the merged companies, to serve as the administrative headquarters for Imperial and International Communications.

The grand opening was preceded by a celebratory luncheon next door to the new building at Accountants' Hall, Lord William Waldorf Astor's one-time London headquarters, built in 1895 and later renamed as 2 Temple Place. The guests were greeted by Lord Inverleith, Chairman of the Marconi Company, who was accompanied by his daughter. The 95 guests represented all the 'Great and the Good' of the merged companies, including, Alfonso (1865–1935), Marconi's elder brother who deputised for the great man, Mr. and Mrs. Edward Wilshaw and the other directors of the company and Sir Herbert Baker, the architect who created the building.

After luncheon, in his speech Lord Inverleith congratulated Sir Herbert on his 'fine work' in designing such a magnificent building. He also said that he looked forward to a return to prosperity for the company. Sir Herbert in reply thanked all the people who had worked so hard to complete the building, and 'all concerned' from the company for all the untiring help he had received. He also spoke of the 'great strides made in the world of communications in the past' and added prophetically that he 'could not even guess what might happen in the next 30 or 60 years'. We can look back at those 60 years and more with the benefit of hindsight, but can no more predict the advances and changes that will occur in the next three or six decades than Sir Herbert could in his time.

The assemblage then traipsed next door where Mrs Denison-Pender was presented with a gold key and a mallet by Lord Inverleith which she then duly tapped against the great double bronze doors, which magically opened to allow access to the couple through the double inner doors into the foyer, past two silent doormen. There were cheers, applause and the flashing of cameras and the guests were then invited into the building too. The party marvelled at the beautifully designed foyer with its green leather sofas and subsequently made their way up to the roof garden which afforded a magnificent view out over the Thames and beyond, with the use of a sizeable telescope if required.

Later, on 3rd September 1933, the Marconi Company, after 21 years at Marconi House, its Strand headquarters, moved to Electra House, Victoria Embankment, occupying the top three floors. According to its own publicity at the time, the new building was 'the most modern office building in Great Britain'. The sixth floor accommodated the management of the company and the departmental chiefs, with Marchese Marconi himself occupying the central room on the front of the building. The new telephone number for the company at Electra House was TEMple Bar 4321 and its telegraphic addresses were Expanse, London for overseas telegrams, and Expanse, Estrand, London for inland ones.

The Marconi Company's offices on the fifth floor were occupied by the Chief Accountant along with the Cashier's Department and various

(Marconi pictured in his office at Electra House in 1934)

comptometer operators, whilst the seventh floor contained the company's research laboratories and in addition the intriguingly named Chief of the Valve Department. A large staff of 'investigators and researchers' was also maintained at the company's Chelmsford establishment in Essex at that time. Another feature of the seventh floor was a permanent display of historical Marconi apparatus, thankfully saved for posterity.

Although the new building primarily housed administrative and accounting departments, for the Marconi and Eastern companies as plans progressed for their complete integration into the new Cables and Wireless company, good use was soon made of the large refectory on the lower ground floor for social functions, and commencing in October 1933, regular staff dances were held there, with the New Year's Eve ball that year being particularly popular and well attended by some 300 or more people. The refectory was fitted with a sprung dance floor, which was later to be boarded over and virtually forgotten about, only to be rediscovered when the building was eventually demolished.

I'm sure Sir John Pender would have been extremely proud of the new headquarters of the combined company. In the following year the company was renamed as Cables and Wireless Ltd, later in May 1934 to be shortened to Cable & Wireless Ltd. Although at the time the company's staff occupied seven different buildings around London, there was no scramble to amalgamate all the sections of the joint company at Victoria Embankment, thus the original Electra House at Moorgate contained the telegraphic operating circuits and the new one primarily the administrative staff, with both retaining the same name. Despite its general lack of telegraph circuits, the new building was very proud to show its best front to the world and in 1935 during the week-long Silver Jubilee celebrations for King George V, the building was graced by a large illuminated 'Cable and Wireless' sign which could be seen from a great distance across the broad sweep of the River Thames.

John Cuthbert Denison-Pender and his wife Irene were at that time living at 65, Eaton Square in London's exclusive Belgravia district. The house was later to find fame as the setting for both television series of *Upstairs, Downstairs*, shot in 1971-75 and 2010-12 respectively. Denison-Pender, following in his grandfather's footsteps, had been an M.P. between 1913 and 1922, representing the constituencies of Newmarket (1913 to 1918, when the constituency was abolished) and Balham and Tooting, a new constituency created in 1918, until 1922, as well as serving in David Lloyd George's First World War government. He retired from politics in 1922 but subsequently enjoyed many high profile company directorships, and later becoming the joint managing-director of Cable and Wireless and a governor of Cable and Wireless Holdings. He was raised to the peerage as Baron Pender of Porthcurnow in 1937.

(Electra House Court Room with Sir John Pender, flanked from left to right by his great-grandson, Lord Pender, his grandson, Lord Pender and his son, Sir John Denison-Pender)

It is worth noting that by 1937 there were then nine cable ships owned by Cable and Wireless in operation around the globe, maintaining some 300,000 miles of submarine cable, with quite a number of lines, though commercially unprofitable, being maintained for strategic purposes. These figures show how the global system of cables in the twentieth century had continued to expand at a tremendous rate as technology improved and the demand for telegrams increased.

1937 brought a year of major change for the Marconi Company. Marconi, who had been unwell for some time after several heart attacks, and who had not been playing much of an active part in running the company for some time, died on 20th July in Rome. Benito Mussolini, the Italian dictator, an old friend who had been best man at Marconi's wedding to his second wife, arranged a state funeral for him. A memorial service was also held for him at Chelmsford Cathedral, attended by Mr. Edward Wilshaw and other dignitaries, and a further central London service was held the next day at St. Peter's, Clerkenwell, the Italian church, attended by other directors of the Marconi and Cable and Wireless companies. As a fitting mark of respect for his passing, all radio-telegraph circuits throughout the world were suspended for two minutes at 1800 hours on 21st July.

Marconi was survived by his first wife, Beatrice (1882-1976), their daughters Degna (1909-1998) and Gioia (1916-1996) (a third daughter, Lucia did not survive childhood) and their son Giulio (1910-1971), and by his second wife Maria Cristina (1900-1994) and their daughter Maria Elettra (b. 1930). The Marconi Company was eventually to move its head office to its manufacturing centre at Chelmsford, Essex where it enjoyed a long period of technological development and production in radio and television.

The 9th November 1937 brought an important visitor to the new Electra House in the shape of the new Lord Mayor of London, the Right Honourable Harry Twyford, as part of the annual Lord Mayor's Show. The mayoral progress, rich in pageantry, consisting of a three-mile long procession of marching bands and floats, dates back 800 years to the reign of King John, when he tried to win the support of the City, by allowing it to choose its own Lord Mayor – providing the new incumbent upon appointment visited the sovereign to swear loyalty.

Cable and Wireless was represented in the parade by two floats – one displaying a slowly revolving eight-foot globe, with red lights flashing on and off to signify the main routes connecting the Empire with the major capitals of the world, the cable routes indicated by red lines and the wireless ones by red dots. The float also accommodated two seamen holding a Lucas cutting and holding grapnel, used for retrieving submarine cables from up to 3,500 fathoms (four miles) deep. On the rear of the tableau was featured a wireless circuit as would be found around the world, with perforator keyboard, Morse key (producing a buzzing sound) and a wireless 'receiving undulator'.

The other float symbolised the binding together of the Empire via business and social telegrams under the sign 'Empire Communications' with the names

(Marchese Marconi, pictured in later life)

and emblems representing the four Dominions – Australia, Canada, New Zealand and South Africa. It also displayed slogans such as *'Oceans Cannot Separate Us'*. The side curtaining of both floats was richly decorated in gold and blue with lions and griffins, symbols of both the Empire and the City of London. Also in the parade, as a sign of the times, was a mobile anti-aircraft gun under the command of Captain Baglehole, better known as 'Bags', from the Chief Accountant's Department at Electra House!

The visit was not just a passing courtesy, as in fact the company was welcoming back one of its own, as Sir Harry had worked in the past for the Eastern Extension Telegraph Company, one of the cable companies which eventually formed Cable and Wireless. A red carpet was laid across the pavement outside the entrance to Electra House and 16 uniformed messenger boys lined the way as a guard of honour. As the Mayor's ornate golden State Coach, pulled by six magnificent horses arrived, Mr. Edward Wilshaw, Chairman and Managing Director of Cable and Wireless Ltd, stepped forward to meet his honoured guest, followed by Lord Inverleith and Lord Pender, respectively President and Chairman of Cable and Wireless (Holding) Ltd. Mr. Wilshaw then presented an Illuminated Address to Sir Harry and introduced his accompanying Lordships to their illustrious guest. In response the Lord Mayor handed Mr. Wilshaw a letter of thanks.

Then as the Mayor's coach was set to depart, eight of the messenger boys filed past, each bearing a red pennant with the name of a telegraph station where Sir Harry had once worked, and they then presented him with congratulatory telegrams with greetings from each of them – Singapore, Hong Kong, Cape St. James (Vietnam), Penang, Banjoewangie (Java), Auckland, Wellington and Porthcurnow. The brief but well-planned visit went perfectly, as was testified by a Cockney voice overheard in the crowd saying, "that went off without a nitch".

A large banner was displayed offering 'Greetings to the Lord Mayor' and whilst directors of the company and their guests filled the ground floor to obtain a grandstand view, staff crowded the windows of the upper floors straining to catch a glimpse of the auspicious occasion.

Electra House, Moorgate was not to be left out of the limelight when in May 1939 it received a visit from Prince George, the then Duke of Kent. The Duke was met by Edward Wilshaw and his fellow directors and given a grand tour of the building. They passed through a Guard of Honour formed by messengers in their distinctive livery, each holding a flag representing one of the colonies or dominions of the Empire. He then toured the operating galleries where he was to receive loyal greetings cabled from the Prime Minister of Australia, this being particularly appropriate as the Duke was at that time Governor-General Designate of Australia.

The Duke was later to be tragically killed in a military aeroplane accident in August 1942, on a 'non-operational' flight whilst flying from Scotland to Iceland. The aircraft, deviating from its intended route, crashed into a Scottish hillside with all those aboard being killed. It was the first death of a member of the Royal Family on active service for 400 years. Some mystery surrounded his mission when a briefcase containing Swedish 100 kronor banknotes was apparently found chained to his wrist – these could not have been officially exchanged in Iceland at the time.

By this time, Edward, later Sir Edward, Wilshaw (1879–1968) was firmly established as chairman of Cable and Wireless, a post he would hold from 1936 to 1947, an extremely important period covering the whole of the Second World War. He began his career as an apprentice with the Eastern Telegraph Company in 1894 and worked his way up through the ranks as an able administrator, and was to play an increasingly important role in the story of Electra House and the history of Cable and Wireless.

Following Adolf Hitler's invasion of Czechoslovakia in March 1938, tensions had risen as it became clear that the Führer's ambitions did not stop there. Later, in September, Neville Chamberlain returned with his famous piece of white paper after signing the Munich Agreement, with his famous quote "peace for our time". But the directors of Cable and Wireless were taking no chances and a reinforced 'gas and bomb proof' emergency operation centre, known as 'The Fortress' was constructed within Electra House, Victoria Embankment, featuring reinforced walls extending from the basement, through the lower ground to the upper ground floor.

In addition overseas circuits were duplicated at the Victoria Embankment building in case the Moorgate building was put out of action by any future enemy action. Thus, as sandbags began to 'decorate' the front entrance to the building on Temple Place, with more taken into Electra House, the management began contacting 1,000 retired staff regarding their re-employment on emergency service. Some 800 promptly accepted the invitation, with the majority of the remainder either being already involved in work of national importance or being medically unfit.

Covering every eventuality, a successful full-scale rehearsal of the move from Moorgate to Temple Place subsequently took place with 1,500 staff taking taxis, buses and underground trains to travel the 1⅓ miles between the two buildings. Little did the participants realise that it would have to be done in earnest in just a few years time, although not at a leisurely pace and not during daylight hours. A second 'fall-back' plan was also made to establish a third option should both Electra Houses be put out of action. An 'unassuming villa' at 12 Hamilton Road in Ealing, west London was set up as a potential command centre to take overall control of the situation, should need arise.

As history tells us, following Hitler's invasion of Poland, Great Britain declared war on Germany on 3rd September 1939 and so began an intense six-year period when accessible and affordable telegrams took on an increasingly important role for government, civilians and the press reporting the conflict. At that time Cable and Wireless was well placed to deal with wartime emergency communication on the home front. It boasted 20 London offices accepting telegrams over the counter, including the two Electra Houses, stretching from the City of London to the entertainment district of the West End as well as 14 provincial offices dotted around the country, including Porthcurno, which sported the rather quaint telephone number of St. Buryan 6. The company's wireless stations at Bodmin, Brentwood, Bridgwater, Dorchester, Ongar, Skegness, Somerton and Tetney also accepted overseas telegrams. Ongar and Dorchester housed transmitters, whilst the others, together with Bearley, near Stratford-upon-Avon were receiving stations. The transmitter at the Rugby wireless station also played a major role over the years.

It was Edward Wilshaw who had instigated the Empire Flat Rate for telegrams on 25th April 1938 after much debate and discussion with all parties concerned, following the precedent of a flat-rate postage rate across the Empire, which had been introduced in 1911. The rate was fixed at 1/3d (one shilling and three-pence) per word. According to Sir Edward's brief memoir *Half a Century of Telecommunications* written for *The Syren and Shipping* magazine in 1944, the rates fifty years earlier in 1894 when he had joined the company were 4/9d (four shillings and nine-pence) per word from London to Australia, 7/9d to Zanzibar and 8/9d to South Africa, all well beyond the pocket of the ordinary man in the street. A year later the Empire Press Rate was introduced at 2¼d (tuppence farthing) per word as well as an Empire Social Telegram Rate, later known as a GLT (Greetings Letter Telegram), which offered the sender 12 words for 5/- (five shillings) with a further 5d (five pence) charged per extra word.

These new rates were followed in 1940 by a 2/6d (two shillings and six-pence) Empire Forces Rate allowing Expeditionary Forces Messages (EFMs)

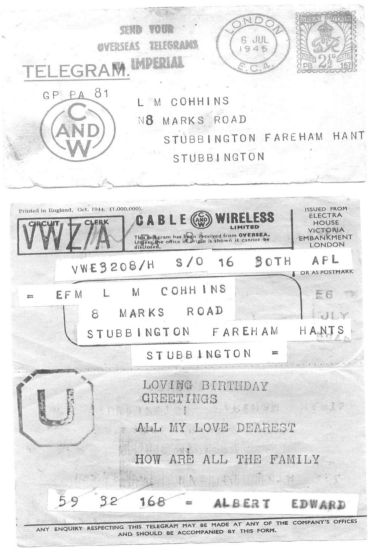

(An EFM message from an anonymous office of origin, with the three chosen text numbers expanded for delivery)

to and from British servicemen, which gave the sender six words for that amount, with the address sent free of charge. A list of 189 numbers under the slogan 'Say it with Numbers' was available to senders, each figure representing a common word or phrase – '1' being 'Letter received, many thanks', and '189' being 'Hope to broadcast greetings from BBC listen X (X being day of the week to be added by filer), and in between various greetings, statements and requests relating to well-being, money, promotion and war damage, etc. By 1942 EFM messages were being sent at the rate of 60 million words per year.

Free messages were also offered in August of that year to and from children evacuated overseas – 'one telegram a month free to Government-evacuated children and their parents'. The CFT (Children's Free Telegrams) service worked in conjunction with the various local overseas telegraph companies especially in Canada and Australia to where thousands of British children had been sent 'out of harm's way'. Within a year between 40,000 and 50,000 such messages were delivered around the world on specially designed message forms portraying children at play on see-saws, swings and riding scooters. For some unknown reason 12 parents and 48 children did not take up the offer that year.

All the new rates introduced since 1938 represented a dramatic shift in the company's charging policy with substantially lower rates, and resulted in millions of people around the world being able to afford to send telegrams for the first time. It was not just a bold move by Edward Wilshaw, but a sensible commercial decision too with a beneficial social outcome especially once the Second World War had begun, with potentially millions of British citizens being displaced and far from home, with a seriously disrupted airmail postage system for the foreseeable future.

In conjunction with the introduction of the new rates in 1940, all the 'Colonial Dependencies' in the Empire were equipped with facilities for wireless transmission and reception, to supplement their existing cable systems – a wise precaution, as cables were open to potential disruption through enemy action.

Sir Edward had been awarded the K.C.M.G. in 1939, following in the illustrious footsteps of Sir John Pender a half a century earlier. He was by then married with two daughters, one of whom Anne, married Flying Officer C. R. 'Ronnie' Driver, D.F.M., (1922-2009), one of the first Allied airmen to be decorated during the Second World War, in March 1940.

(Sir Edward off to the Palace perhaps?)

Ronnie had been the front gunner in a Lancaster bomber, which had taken a pasting during a raid over enemy territory. As it limped home he extinguished a fire in the aeroplane, saving it from certain destruction only for it to ditch into the North Sea on its way back to England. Ronnie was instrumental in launching the life raft and helping his crew members to safety. Sadly his fellow gunner in the aircraft, and best friend, was killed in the raid and Ronnie no doubt felt tremendous guilt at his own survival, to the extent that he subsequently threw his medal into the Thames and was to suffer post-traumatic stress for years to come. Ronnie was later to become the father of Hollywood actress Minnie Driver, although as the result of his later relationship with Gaynor Millington.

Sir Edward Wilshaw was well known during the war for being 'chauffeured' around London in an old-fashioned Hansom Cab, pulled by a handsome well-groomed horse. It was his statement to the world about saving vital petrol supplies for the war effort, and you can also be sure he enjoyed the attention it received when he went out for a 'spin'. He used the cab for over two years, finally giving it up in the summer of 1945, as he was eventually persuaded to accept exclusive use of a company car – which he insisted should be a Rolls-Royce!

Chapter Three

Electra Houses At War

With the outbreak of hostilities between Britain and Germany on 3rd September 1939, all Overseas Telegraph Operators (OTOs) in England were 'frozen' in their jobs, as being a qualified OTO was classified as a 'Reserved Occupation'. As early as May 1939 other, 'non-manip' (non-manipulation or non-operating) employees were encouraged to enlist or to join the Territorial Army, whilst operators and administration staff were trained as ARP (Air Raid Precautions) officers and first-aiders. Only much later in the war were 350 employees based at Electra House, Victoria Embankment, and aged under 35, who were engaged in ancillary duties, conscripted for active military service. Many operators had wished to join up from the outset but were not allowed to as they were performing 'vital war work'.

At the beginning of the Second World War, Cable and Wireless operated 155,000 of the 350,000 miles of cable that spanned the world, together with some 130 permanent wireless circuits. As countries fell into enemy hands circuits would be mothballed for the duration. When Italy entered the war in June 1940, she cut all five Gibraltar to Malta cables and in retaliation the Italian cables to Spain and South America were cut on behalf of the Allies by the *CS Mirror*.

In the Far East in February 1942 the fall of Singapore, overrun by the Japanese, caused extensive disruption to the company's communications network, as it was a major cable station handling traffic to the Far East, Australia and New Zealand and had provided the fastest and most efficient route for traffic. This necessitated diverting traffic either via Canada and the Pacific or via the west coast of Africa via Cape Town and the Cocos Islands, thus demonstrating the versatility of the network.

The Cocos Islands had witnessed dramatic events during the First World War, when in November 1914 the German light cruiser the *SMS Emden* had attacked and disabled the telegraph station on Direction Island. Before a party from the ship could land to destroy the equipment, a distress call had been sent out, and the Australian cruiser *HMAS Sydney*, arrived in all haste to tackle the German ship. The *Emden* was destroyed with the loss of 134 crew members, with the *Sydney* losing four of its complement.

From 1920 the *Official Secrets Act* had compelled all cable companies to supply copies of all traffic it handled to the government and in due course telephone lines of foreign embassies were also to be monitored at Electra House, Moorgate, until the building was damaged by German bombing, and then the 'new' Electra House took over.

But prior to this, Electra House at Victoria Embankment had another role to play. Under the direction of Sir Colin Campbell Stuart, *Department EH*, was set up in room 207.

On the night of 3rd September after Germany had invaded Poland and Britain declared war, the department produced an aerial propaganda leaflet, over five million copies of which were dropped on Bremen, Hamburg and nine cities of the Ruhr by three Whitley bombers from 51 Squadron R.A.F. and seven from 58 Squadron. The leaflet was titled: Warning: *A Message from Great Britain* and it addressed itself to *"German Men and Women"* stating that the Reich had forced war upon Great Britain and pointing out that Hitler had gone back on the peaceful intentions he had expressed the previous April. With prescience it warned that their rulers *"had condemned them to massacres, miseries and privations of a war they cannot ever hope to win"*. A copy of the leaflet with the full German text and English translation is on display at the Imperial War Museum in London.

This and other leaflets were produced at *'Department EH'*, or to give it its full title, *'the Department for Propaganda in Enemy Countries'* at Electra House, Victoria Embankment. Campbell Stewart, who continued to head the organisation, had played such an important role a decade earlier in effecting the amalgamation of the various wireless and cables companies which were to become Cable and Wireless Ltd. He had previously been deputy director, under Lord Northcliffe, of a similar propaganda department towards the end of the First World War. The original organisation had worked out of the London residence of the Marquis of Crewe in Curzon Street.

When *Department EH* was absorbed with other shadowy organisations into the SOE (Special Operations Executive) in the latter part of 1940, Campbell Stewart resigned and devoted himself to his role on the Imperial Communications Advisory Committee, which was to become the Commonwealth Communications Council, of which he was made Chairman, in April 1944. When Cable and Wireless was nationalised in 1945 he resigned, remaining as a director of *The Times* newspaper in London until 1960. He died aged 87 in 1972.

A later connection between the overseas telegraph service and the government of the day was facilitated by the company supplying overseas telegraphists to run a small department at the Ministry of Information, later renamed the Central Office of Information (COI) and based at Lambeth in south London. This co-operation lasted from the 1940s until the end of March 1983, when, in a cost-cutting exercise, the work was put out to tender. The operators running the system were highly competent and trusted to handle much sensitive information, especially in times of intense government activity such as during the 1982 'Falkland's Conflict'. The COI was finally wound up following spending cuts by the Conservative-Liberal Democrat Coalition government as recently as December 2011.

With the British Army's retreat from Dunkirk in 1940, thousands of weapons had been abandoned in France, depleting the army's resources, and it was decided in May 1941 to hold 'War Weapons Week', such as that which had proved so successful during the First World War, to raise investment from both the public and private companies to replenish the country's stock of weaponry. Sir Edward Wilshaw, representing the Cable and Wireless board, announced that the company would be contributing £1,000,000 to the fund, no small sum at that time. The company's patriotism was never in doubt but it's likely that such a grand gesture helped maintain the Company's independence from British government control not least during wartime, and it continued with its freedom to operate as a private commercial enterprise, albeit whilst working closely with the authorities, until the end of the war.

The Bombing of Electra House, Moorgate

It would be eight years, almost to the day, after the new Electra House at Victoria Embankment had been opened, that the Moorgate building was hit by the Luftwaffe in a raid on the night of Saturday 10th May 1941. Incendiary bombs caused extensive damage, ironically on the night of the last major raid of the London Blitz. The adjacent Tower Chambers was also set alight, adding to the problem. The dramatic events of that fateful night were recounted in minute detail three years later by John McGeorge in his memoir printed in the June 1944 edition of *'The Zodiac'*, the Cable and Wireless house magazine.

A 'phone call was received warning of a 'City Yellow' and a spotter was dispatched to the roof of the building in readiness to check for any fires from incendiary bombs. Then at 11pm the wailing of an air-raid siren was heard, the 'Moaning Minnie' as it was known, which even now engenders a feeling of fear and dread in those old enough to remember the war. One would live in hope that it was a false alarm and that the *'All-Clear'*, or *'Raiders Passed'* would be sounded shortly afterwards, but that night it was not to be. The Roof Patrol is reinforced and before midnight the raid commences 'sending a shower of incendiaries over the building'. The alarm is raised and patrols search for any fires or damage but nothing is detected, until fifteen minutes later when flame is spotted by the patrol, shooting upwards from the Facsimile Room on the top floor of Tower Chambers, three floors below their vantage point on the neighbouring Electra House roof.

The well-drilled squads raced to the Facsimile Room to try to control and extinguish the fire using stirrup pumps but the fire was soon out of control and a request was then put through to City Control for assistance from the Auxiliary Fire Service to tackle the fire. Meanwhile all fire doors between Tower Chambers and Electra House were closed to try to contain the fire as the team used what water they could transport from the lavatories to fight the blaze. Then the floor of the Facsimile Room gave way, crashing down into the old 'Local Room' below, as a report is received that the fire has jumped the gap between the buildings on the second floor and has spread to Electra House. The decision is then made to abandon efforts to save Tower Chambers and to concentrate on Electra House. All the in-house fire-fighters then concentrated their efforts with some success, to stem the spread of the flames and a second call for assistance to City Control is made, pointing out that there are 1,700 gallons of paraffin, 200 gallons of heavy oil and 20 gallons of petrol stored in the basement of the building beneath the fire!

At 00.34 the first fire engine arrived from the Auxiliary Fire Service and the seasoned Blitz-hardened fire officers take control, running three water hoses up the Electra House stair wells, but sadly there is no water pressure, no doubt due to bomb damage to water mains in the City. A fourth hose is trained on the fire from another side of the building but only a trickle of water is available. By now the second and third floors of Tower Chambers are engulfed in flames and the fire is rapidly spreading down to the first floor. The fire on the Electra House side was still being kept at bay until it was realised that the fire had spread to upper floors and it was decided that the gallant 'dozen amateurs with stirrup-pumps' could do no more and should withdraw and leave matters to the professionals. Work then began on desperately salvaging valuable equipment from the galleries.

Then, as most of the equipment had been removed by a chain of people, an almighty crash was heard, windows were blown in and falling masonry was everywhere. It wasn't known at the time but Salisbury House, an adjacent building, had received a direct hit from a bomb. The resulting explosion turned Electra House, stripped of its doors and windows, into a vast funnel of flame as the raging inferno rushed upwards. A quick inspection showed that it was now a major conflagration and all that could be done was to evacuate the building, and all staff were instructed to proceed across the road to the safety of Moorgate Underground station. All personnel were accounted for with no fatalities, although there were some close shaves and some very shaken staff members, who had fought so bravely to combat the blaze on a night they would never forget.

By 0200 McGeorge and a handful of staff members remained to watch over the stricken building. By then the initial fire engine had been augmented by three others, with a water tower working on Tower Chambers from nearby London Wall. At no time was the Fire Brigade able to engage with the fire in Electra House due to the extreme danger posed by the fuel stores, which thankfully had not ignited. The Fire Brigade officer had asked for twenty appliances to be sent but no doubt the service was stretched to breaking point dealing with hundreds of other 'call-outs' on that fateful night and his request went unanswered.

By 0420 the smoke had cleared sufficiently to allow an inspection of the upper floors of Electra House as the intensity of the blaze subsided, leaving 'an angry glowing shell, with smouldering fires creeping slowly northwards'. With volunteers returning from the Underground station shelter, stirrup-pump parties continued to battle the continuing smaller fires, with some success, saving some of the offices on the third floor and the old boardroom on the second. Under McGeorge's guidance they continued working until 10am when the last bucket of water was used up just as the day staff came to relieve them, handing over with "phones gone, lights gone, gas gone, half the b***** building gone". As a final insult the police then ordered a complete evacuation of the area due to the discovery of an unexploded bomb in nearby Finsbury Circus.

All in all, it was a night of individual heroism, which amazingly resulted in no fatalities, in no small measure due to the actions of McGeorge who as a result was awarded the British Empire Medal (BEM) for gallantry, which he was presented with at his investiture in April 1944. As we shall see, as the war progressed, his heroic actions did not end there.

One young eyewitness to the devastation, the morning after, was a teenaged new recruit named Richard Cannon. Having spent his first day of training with the company on the Friday before the bombing, he threaded his way on the Monday morning through the sparse road traffic and the fire engines, still mopping up after the air raid, as he walked from London Bridge station across London Bridge, past the Bank of England to Moorgate, the air still thick with the smell of burning wood. Imagine his shock at finding that much of the abandoned Electra House and Tower Chambers buildings were just bombed out shells.

A chalked notice on a blackboard informed him 'all C & W staff to V.E.'. This meant little to the young man, but a passer-by informed him that 'V.E.' referred to the other Electra House situated along the Victoria Embankment, by Temple Gardens and the Temple Underground station. Nothing daunted, he set off on foot to find it, only to be stopped en route by a policeman who informed him that there were unexploded bombs ahead. He decided to risk it and pressed ahead, eventually reporting for duty on the 6th floor of the new building, to be met by his training instructor with the unsympathetic greeting of 'you're late!'

Until that time the sixth floor of the building had lain empty for some time after its earlier occupancy by the Marconi Company, but it was soon to be established as the new company training school, under the guidance of a Mr. Smith, the Principal, (curiously nicknamed '*the Prawn*', apparently as a prank by a young trainee). The young Dick Cannon was to play his part in rescuing whatever equipment could be salvaged from the old building. After receiving permission from the Fire Brigade to enter the stricken building, the 'rescue squad' entered the old training school in the basement to salvage any vital equipment that could be reused, once it had been stripped down and reconditioned. Tables, chairs, work benches, etc were also scrounged from here and there around the new building to outfit the new school. It was a time of considerable adjustment for everyone concerned with all the operating circuits being positioned in 'The Fortress' in the lower floors of the new building, and therefore better protected from and less susceptible to more bombing.

And what, you may wonder became of the young Richard Cannon? After completing his training and gaining valuable experience at Electra House, like many of his contemporaries, he was sent overseas to a foreign cable station, in his case to Ascension Island in the South Atlantic. Reaching the station during wartime was not easy, as you can imagine, and it involved a somewhat perilous journey on a small Free-French freighter, through the submarine-infested waters of the Bay of Biscay, then down the coast of West Africa to Ghana, to await a lift to Ascension from a U.S. bomber, which was then being used as a troop carrier.

Cannon survived the war and spent sixteen years in overseas service for the company before returning to continue his career in the U.K., rising to become the Joint-Managing Director of Cable and Wireless Ltd. in 1977, it, in the meantime, having re-located its offices from Electra House to Mercury House in Theobalds Road less than a mile away. He further progressed to become sole Managing Director before retiring in 1982. Dick Cannon, now in his early 90s, is still very active at the time of writing.

Electra House, Moorgate was then abandoned as an operational station with all circuits having been transferred to the 'new' Electra House building under the contingency plan, and as the operating circuits had been duplicated at the Victoria Embankment building there was a minimum of disruption to services. With the loss of Electra House Moorgate, operating and administrative operations were then finally all housed under the one roof.

This was not quite the end for the company's use of the old building. In January 1943 a temporary girls' training school was set up in the basement of the burned out building, with 650 girls and women passing through it as they completed their training of up to a year. It must have been quite an eerie experience for the trainees, but during wartime there was an air of acceptance of sometimes-strange occurrences, as one never quite knew what life (or the

Luftwaffe) would throw at you next. The boys' training school was still maintained at the Victoria Embankment building, despite losing part of its facilities to later bomb damage.

The Moorgate building was eventually repaired and restored and in 1944 was occupied by the City of London College and subsequently sold in 1948 to the London County Council (LCC), which eventually led to its current use as part of the London Metropolitan University. Tower Chambers was also repaired and continued in use for some years as a counter office, still accepting overseas telegrams.

In October 1941, as a German invasion of Britain seemed a distinct possibility, the Home Secretary and the Minister of Home Security produced their *'Invasion Preparations by Civil Departments'*, a Top Secret document 'to be kept under lock and key'. It was written to share with members of the War Cabinet detailed plans in the event of such an invasion. The section covering 'Overseas Cable and Radio Services' referred to Cable and Wireless services at Electra House, Victoria Embankment, as well as those available through Western Union and Commercial Cable in the City, as well as the Central Telegraph Office in the City, the headquarters of the inland telegram service. Should any of these offices be put out of action, then reserve facilities had been 'provided and equipped in the suburbs', and as a last resort services could be maintained at cable heads and radio stations.

At that time government departments had direct teleprinter links to the cable companies, but should those links be severed, the Post Office and the cable companies were to provide arrangements for delivering telegrams by hand if necessary. Alternative links to the cable heads and radio stations had been created, avoiding towns, which might be subject to bombing. The report continued that 'if any or all submarine cables are cut at sea, sufficient radio capacity has already been provided' to maintain essential government communications. Signals for *'Action Stations'* or to *'Stand To'* had also been agreed with the cable companies, to enable them to put their staff and operating procedures on an emergency footing.

Luckily the invasion never came and as the war progressed communications between the British government and its overseas forces were maintained although sometimes with operating staff and overseas circuits at full stretch. With such an extensive network Cable and Wireless could always go 'the long way around' if necessary, to reach a distant destination, perhaps cut off by enemy action.

COMMUNICATIONS
OLD AND NEW

3. — MESSAGES BY FIRE

A SPECTACULAR method of swiftly conveying information over great distances, and one that survived up to quite recent times even in our own country, was the lighting of beacons on the hill-tops. The many Beacon Hills you will find dotted about the map still preserve in their name this ancient system of communication.

Britain's Blaze of Beacons

Our ancestors lit beacons to tell of the landing of Cæsar's legions. When the great Armada swept up the English Channel, Britain blazed with beacons from South to North, from East to West. In 1804, Sir Walter Scott tells of a chain of beacons from the Scottish hills that raised a huge army to challenge a much-heralded invader who never came.

The March of Progress

In the middle of the 19th century began the great work of invention and pioneering in the field of cable and wireless communication that has made it possible to send a message from London to New York and get a reply back within 24 seconds. In this amazing development Cable and Wireless Ltd. has played the leading part, linking the British Empire and the world by a system of overseas telegraphy that is swift, sure, and inexpensive.

CABLE AND WIRELESS LTD

The only British owned and operated Overseas Telegraph Company in this country

(Punch Magazine, October 1941)

Life during wartime at Electra House on the Victoria Embankment, was not all 'doom and gloom' with overloaded circuits and long hours. A silver band comprised of uniformed messengers, had been formed in January 1942 and they were always ready to perform a morale-boosting concert for the staff, or to entertain visiting dignitaries – dignitaries such as the exiled King Haakon of Norway in 1944 or newly-elected Lord Mayors of the City of London who seem to have put a visit to Electra House on their itinerary since that of Harry Twyford in 1937. Each would be accorded due deference, being met by Sir Edward Wilshaw and his Court of Directors with a Guard of Honour provided by uniformed messengers, entertained to a lavish luncheon and given a guided tour of operating circuits, with an opportunity to exchange fraternal greetings with the Lord Mayor of a distant overseas city.

The band, originally conceived as a 'drum and fife band' was eventually shaped and honed as a brass band by Arthur Irons (1901–1994), a telegraph operator, who had drawn attention to himself by conducting the Tottenham Hotspur band at football matches on Saturdays at White Hart Lane. The 24 members of the silver band were encouraged by an extra allowance of two shillings a week, and the band was to flourish well into the 1970s, still proudly calling itself the 'Cable and Wireless Band', despite the company's change of nomenclature in the meantime. They were regular performers at Christmas carol concerts, with Mr. Irons at the helm for 30 years or more. They were also featured on the popular BBC radio programme '*In Town Tonight*' in 1942, and later were to play before the then Princess Elizabeth and Prince Philip at a Hyde Park Pageant.

Other diversions, such as an annual staff art exhibition, were instituted, with a photographic exhibition to follow at a later date.

The war years heralded a great expansion in services, as fighting on various fronts evolved and telegraphic needs changed with them. By 1942 an extra 52 wireless circuits had been set up, partly to replace those lost to Japanese occupation but also to follow the direction of the war, with seven wireless circuits alone set up from London to Cairo to cope with the amount of traffic to and from the North African theatre of operations. At the same time picture transmission services had been established to Moscow and Cairo to cope with the hunger for images of the war in those areas by the world's press. Another complication at that time due to the Japanese occupation of parts of the Far East, was the extreme shortage of Gutta Percha for submarine cable work, as most of the world's supply now lay in occupied territory, and those supplies still available in the West had to be carefully husbanded to cope with any new cable laying or repairing.

Electra House also had to cope with nearly 60 direct circuits to government ministries, newspapers and press agencies, most requiring 24-hour a day staffing. Government censorship of press telegrams had been instituted at the start of the war to control the release of any sensitive information that might in any way help the enemy, and it would continue in operation until September 1945.

February 1944 saw Sir Edward Wilshaw celebrate 50 years service with the company. The occasion was marked by a grand reception at the Savoy Hotel in The Strand and it was attended by all the directors and senior managers of Cable and Wireless. Sir Edward was presented with a gold watch, a copy of his portrait in oils which graced the Court Room, and two elaborately bound books, one containing greetings from staff at all the company's stations around the world, and a second which contained the signatures of all the staff at London Station, Electra House.

He was to retain his contact with the company for the rest of his life, watching it evolve, as it had always done, embracing the latest technology to meet the communication needs of the day.

THE ZODIAC

THE STAFF JOURNAL OF CABLE AND WIRELESS LIMITED

No. 423   Vol. 36   March, 1944   Sixpence

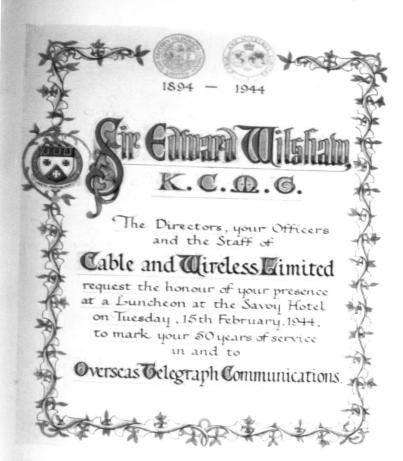

(Front page of The Zodiac, March 1944)

The Bombing of Electra House, Victoria Embankment

Three years after the firebombing of the Moorgate building, at precisely 3.40 a.m. on the morning of 24th July 1944, the 'new' Electra House was also on the receiving end of German bombing when a V1 flying bomb, a 'Doodlebug', hit the eastern corner of the building. It severely damaged the first, second and third floors, destroying the Chairman's apartment and severely damaging the chapel on the second floor. The chapel had been provided for quiet contemplation, at the request of staff members, by Sir Edward and it had been dedicated by the Archbishop of Canterbury, Cosmo Gordon Lang, two years previously on 25th February 1942. The bronze doors, inscriptions and memorial tablets in the chapel were badly damaged but miraculously the altar survived intact. The tablets contained the names of 446 staff members who had fallen in the First World War, and as yet, just 23 who had died on active service in the then present conflict.

Luckily, the chairman and his wife, Sir Edward and Lady Myn Wilshaw, unusually, were not in residence at the time, a rare occurrence for him in those days. However, there were staff fatalities. Of the 400 or so staff on night duty at the time, according to the official status report at the time, now preserved at the Westminster Archives in Central London, three people were killed and eleven were taken for treatment to the Charing Cross hospital, just off The Strand, five being detained.

The dead were named as 'H. Scholfield, Charles Hardy and May Victoria Devonshire' although strangely, contemporary reports in *The Zodiac* magazine made no mention of H. Scholfield. Perhaps in the confusion on that fateful night they were missing, presumed dead, but subsequently turned up alive. Sadly Mr. Hardy and Mrs. Devonshire had been sheltering in the approved bomb shelter below pavement level when tons of masonry had fallen on it.

Those detained in hospital were P. Braybrooke, L. Bell (night watchman), A. Turner, Miss Ethel Peel and Mrs. Kathleen Adams. Four others with injuries, F. R. Palmer, Mrs. Butler, A. E. Willcock and H. Smith were treated at the hospital, and then sent home. Three others were treated at the scene, Miss Woolfard and Miss Jones for shock and an unnamed LRP (Light Rescue Post) man. Thus the total of 17 casualties among some 400 night workers could have been much worse.

Several people had lucky escapes, not least a woman operator, caught in the ladies lavatory at the time, who was dug out virtually unscathed.

(Aftermath of the bombing with sentry on guard)

Doodlebugs, launched from the French and Dutch coasts, were rocket powered flying bombs with just enough fuel to reach their intended target, generally London. Of the 9,521 launched, some 2,000 reached the capital, destroying or damaging up to 100,000 houses, although a mere 17 hit the square mile of the City of London, together with high explosive bombs, parachute mines, oil bombs and countless incendiary bombs plus and not least, two V2 rockets in the final days of the end of the war. The City lost more than a quarter of its buildings to destruction by bombing or through being too badly damaged to escape subsequent demolition.

The first V1 arrived on 13th June 1944 and they continued to wreak havoc and cause considerable loss of life and destruction until October 1944 when the last sites within range of London were overrun by the allied armies, following the D-Day invasion of 6th June. It is a credit to the anti-aircraft batteries, the Barrage Balloon Command and the use of high-speed fighter aircraft by the R.A.F. to intercept them, that many more flying bombs did not reach their intended targets.

In a news report published two months after the bombing of Electra House in the *West Australian* newspaper, after the censors had released the information, more details of the Electra House bombing were made available. Quoting a telegram received from Sir Edward the newspaper stated that "Telegrams for transmission overseas were delayed less than 30 minutes. The bomb crashed head on into the building and the shock was felt half a mile away…the blast threw the main power supply out of action, but less than 10 minutes later the emergency plant was running, and within half an hour all messages were cleared, without reception terminals throughout the Empire and foreign countries suspecting that the headquarters of the Imperial overseas telegraphs system had suffered severe damage from enemy action". The telegram went on to say there had been two fatalities, rather than three, supporting the report in the October 1944 edition of *The Zodiac.*

The report continued, saying that the roof spotters Tom Bradshaw and H. T. Fickling "having given an Immediate Danger (ID) signal as they saw the flaming bomb hurtling towards the building, saved many lives by risking their own to telephone a last minute 'lie flat' warning, which was broadcast from the ARP room by John McGeorge, Assistant Controller, one second before the bomb hit". The report continued, "The bomb penetrated the flat in which Sir Edward and Lady Wilshaw along with Admiral H. W. Grant, the chairman of the Marconi Company, and his wife would normally have been sleeping. A maid, Connie Woolgar, sleeping alone in the third floor flat, was dug out almost unhurt from the rubble. Another person, Joe Cox, who had retired from the accounts department, but who had returned to fire-watch at his old firm, had been resting above the flat when the bomb struck. "Clambering out of the debris he groped his way in darkness through broken glass, fallen doors and twisted metal. He then extinguished a fire single-handed before reporting for further duty". A cordon was quickly set up around the building by the Home Guard and an emergency treatment centre was set up in the refectory on the lower ground floor.

A woman doctor rushed immediately to the scene to help, and by 6.30 a.m., Dr. Eric Bayley, the Company Medical Officer, arrived to treat shock cases. Bayley had spent many a night sleeping in his surgery on the fourth floor during air-raids, but ironically and luckily, not that night. He was reported as saying that he was "astounded at the calm, efficient way all operators and other staff carried on". It was also reported that Press Liaison Officer Frank Waters and his colleagues whose duty it was to help correspondents get messages through quickly, were searching their ruined room next morning when a telephone rang. They dug it out of the rubble, taking the call from a correspondent enquiring about his cablegram. They calmly answered the query then went back to clearing the rubble of their office. It seems the wartime spirit and unflappable British ability to cope with all situations was very much in evidence, no doubt with the aid of gallons of tea.

A further report added that the Chairman's office, one of the training schools, the offices of RCA, the American communications and recording company, the Public Relations and the Press Liaison offices and the Boys' Training School had all been destroyed. For some time after the event Sir Edward could be seen, usually in denim overalls, working from the Court Room whilst other displaced officials found offices where they could. The Chairman's flat and office, the 'Blue Room', had contained Sir Edward's precious collection of Chinese porcelain and ironically perhaps, Dresden china, which was reduced to rubble with the rest of the room's contents. Later in the day, upon surveying the damage to his quarters his wry comment was *"Well, all I can say, thank God, it hit the least important part of the building"*.

(Picking up the pieces in the aftermath)

Despite the serious damage to the building, as emergency power was switched on and the operating circuits were working again within minutes, the Civil Defence report stated that 'although Electra House is considerably damaged by blast, communications are all in working order'. Accountants' Hall, at 2, Temple Place, immediately adjacent to Electra House, also suffered severe blast damage from the bomb with the report at the time stating 'water running into basement…stopcock is under debris'.

The work on clearing the debris began almost immediately with the displaced Home Guard boys from the demolished training school salvaging what they could and throwing "broken brickwork, smashed furniture and soaked papers into the street". Within a few days they shifted an estimated 300 tons of debris! Once this task had been completed builders began erecting scaffolding for the work of repairing the building to begin.

The press were quick to congratulate the staff for coping with the situation and for the way in which the service offered to them was virtually uninterrupted. The London head of the *Australian Consolidated Press* expressing his admiration and sympathy for those on duty at the time of the bombing, added "I know the severity of the attack; the explosion nearly blew me out of bed, half a mile away!" Similar plaudits were received from editors of *The Times*, *The Daily* and *Sunday Express*, *The Star* and other daily newspapers. Once the censors had released the story and overseas stations could be notified of events, messages of sympathy and support began to flow in from around the world. To the overseas Cable and Wireless staff, London Station was not just the telegraphic hub they worked with on a daily basis, but also the symbolic heart of the company and system, which engendered respect and affection from them.

Electra House suffered no further war damage and was repaired by the end of the war, and continued its role as the world's clearing-house for telegrams into the austere years of the post-war recovery.

The two Electra Houses were not the only 'telegraphic casualties' of bombing during the Second World War with the Central Telegraph Office in St. Martin's Le Grand being seriously damaged, and even some of the post-war Area Offices were to be built on or close to bomb sites. But whatever Hitler threw at them, the resilience of the people and the systems ensured that the overseas telegraph service survived and prospered.

The need for telegrams continued to be strong in the post-war years as the long slow road to rebuilding the world's financial systems took place and British businesses began to pick up the pieces and the need for renewed

(On the mend with Union 'Jack' flying defiantly, December 1944)

contact with the outside world began to increase. In those pre-Common Market days Britain's trade with the Empire and North and South America was particularly important and telephone calls were very expensive and not always easy to connect. So the telegram continued its role in providing government and commercial communication and for contact between families across the far-flung British Empire, as well as providing an important link between our armed forces and their loved ones at home. It was estimated that in 1943 alone the British government sent 250 million words *'Via Imperial'*.

1944 found Sir Edward Wilshaw undertaking a 'Grand Tour' of cable and wireless stations around the Mediterranean. He visited Athens, Rome and Marseilles, all recently liberated by the Allies, as well as Cairo, Casablanca and Gibraltar. He was warmly welcomed at all the stations, some of which had been out of touch till recently with London Station for several years. Cable and Wireless stations had been prime targets for invading armies, and there had been some last minute evacuations with valuable equipment taken to safety or destroyed or hidden for the duration of the war. It was now in everyone's interests to re-establish cable and radio links especially with many thousands of Allied troops keen to maintain contact with families in the UK.

From 'D' Day, 6th June 1944, until 5th December, six months later, a huge volume of traffic was handled at London Station, with 46.5 million words sent in press telegrams alone, with 8,950 photo-telegrams sent in addition.

The contrast in the total number of words handled between 1938 and 1944 was predictably dramatic with a rise in government messages from 12 million words to 260 million, an increase of over 2,000%! At the same time press wordage rose from 29 million to 139 million, a 383% rise, whilst social and greetings messages accounted for a rise of 1,559%, from 3 million to 49 million! At one time during the Second World War, as resources were stretched and some overseas circuits were liable to become swamped with messages, poster campaigns were launched asking the public to 'Telegraph less' and to 'Telephone less'. But despite the mammoth challenges presented to the company, it was equal to the task despite loss of staff, due to call-ups especially later in the war, and not forgetting shortages of equipment and the bombing of the London Stations. It was a remarkable achievement, and a vindication of the government's decision to allow Cable and Wireless to remain as a private company throughout the war.

Due to the vital nature of telegrams and the consequent large volume sent during the Second World War, Cable and Wireless made a handsome profit of

SHE KNEW THAT
DADDY WAS WATCHING

Distance no longer means separation ! Each week, over a vast network of oversea routes, flash hundreds of thousands of personal messages. Just one small part of the enormous traffic in world communications handled by CABLE AND WIRELESS LTD.

★ ★ ★

When you cable, mark your cable 'Via Imperial.' See that your correct Christian name or initials are telegraphed with your surname. Uncertainty as to sender's identity causes anxiety.

CABLE AND WIRELESS LIMITED · ELECTRA HOUSE · LONDON

WHEN JACK
GOT HIS MEDAL
THEY WERE THERE

100,000 personal messages a week keep the Forces in touch with home . . . a small part of the enormous traffic in words flashing round the world over the vast network of CABLE AND WIRELESS routes.

★ ★ ★

When you cable, mark your cable 'Via Imperial.' Only telegraph essential particulars or address. Unnecessary words waste time and money.

CABLE AND WIRELESS LIMITED · ELECTRA HOUSE · LONDON

(Cable and Wireless advertising from early 1945 in Aeroplane magazine)

just under £1.38m. in 1944, an increase on the previous year. And in that year 705 million messages were handled, against 231 million in 1939, including 2,000 photo-telegrams a month, against 100 at the start of the conflict. This figure reflected the newspapers' insatiable demand for pictures of the war for their front pages. In his Chairman's report for the 1945 AGM, Sir Edward claimed, "he knew of no case where a message failed to be delivered due to an air-raid; all messages being delivered by car or bicycle". He also noted, that "despite the Mediterranean cable east of Malta being cut by the Italians and the fact that the Japanese had taken over several stations in the Far East, 47 new wireless circuits had been opened during the war allowing for continuity of service to many far-flung destinations". He also praised the company's cable ships, which had bravely stayed continuously at sea repairing cables throughout the war.

As the war in Europe came to a close, the Blue Train or Mobile Wireless Assembly (MWA), a portable wireless telegraph station, which consisted of five vans and a trailer had followed the British army especially as the Allies pushed northwards through Italy. It followed the withdrawal of German troops from Italy, moving from Udine in Northern Italy to Klagenfurt in Austria before being diverted south to Trieste. It was subsequently to be transferred to Jerusalem, where the British Mandate to run the country was being challenged by Jewish insurgents, which culminated in the establishment of the State of Israel in 1948, after much blood was shed. The Blue Train service was finally withdrawn in March 1946, sending its last message to London Station from Vienna.

Victory over Japan was still some way off as the Allies fought to regain territory in the Far East and the Pacific. The company sent out special Telcom (Telegraphic Communications) units to countries such as Burma (now Myanmar), Singapore and Ceylon (now Sri Lanka) to provide telegraphic facilities for the forces and press in particular.

Once the Japanese had surrendered, following the dropping of atomic bombs over Hiroshima and Nagasaki and the terrible devastation they caused, the full horrors of the Japanese prisoner of war camps were made plain. For its part, in 1945, Cable and Wireless delivered 180,000 telegrams free of charge to anxious relatives, mostly in Great Britain, waiting for news of loved ones who had served in the Far East.

A covering letter from Sir Edward Wilshaw was sent with telegrams from servicemen stating "It is a great pleasure to me to be able to send you the enclosed copy of a telegram from your relative who is now liberated from the Japanese". It went on to say "in order to relieve your anxiety at the earliest possible moment this message has been sent free of charge by Cable and Wireless Ltd. from the Far East, and by the Post Office, in co-operation with

FROM SIR EDWARD WILSHAW, K.C.M.G.
CHAIRMAN

ELECTRA HOUSE,
VICTORIA EMBANKMENT,
LONDON, W.C.2.

Dear Sir or Madam,

It is a great pleasure to me to be able to send you the enclosed copy of a telegram from your relative who is now liberated from the Japanese.

In order to relieve your anxiety at the earliest possible moment this message has been transmitted free of charge by Cable and Wireless Ltd. from the Far East, and by the Post Office, in co-operation with the War Office.

In the same way we shall be happy to send your reply free, if you will write it - using about 12 words in addition to the address - on the enclosed form and hand it in at your local Cable and Wireless Office or any Post Office where telegrams are normally accepted.

Will you please insert on the reply-paid form the address given in the enclosed telegram and sign it with your surname.

With best wishes,
I remain,
Yours sincerely,

Edward Wilshaw

Chairman.

(A kind offer from Sir Edward to families of released POWs)

the War Office". The letter invited relatives to send a reply of "about 12 words in addition to the address" free of charge from any Cable and Wireless office or Post Office that accepted telegrams. Commencing 31st August 1945 in Colombo, Ceylon (now Sri Lanka), the many thousands of such telegrams were sent *gratis*. This generous gesture reflected a similar offer for prisoners of war released from European POW camps following the defeat of Germany in 1944.

After the Japanese surrender 18,200 miles of submarine cable in the Far East was returned to company control, along with 11 Cable and Wireless stations. Also at that time 61 members of staff were unaccounted for, many having been interned by the Japanese with fate then unknown.

Considerable work was required before the system to and from the Far East would return to its pre-war status. In fact, it wasn't until 1949 that a direct cable link with Hong Kong was re-established, the first time since 1941.

(14 year-old Peter Nutt, proudly wearing his messenger's uniform in 1945)

Chapter Four

Post-War Days

(Flags flying for post-war Victory celebrations, June 1946)

The Internal Layout of Electra House

The internal layout of Electra House at Temple Place was liable to change throughout the history of the use of the building as requirements arose to accommodate new systems driven by changes in technology and the expansion of the service as more circuits were linked to the system. In addition, as a service might become more or less popular, the space required for it would need to be expanded or contracted accordingly.

A typical layout of the building in the early post-war period went from the basement equipped with generator, strong-room, workshops and even a cinema and projector room, up to the seventh floor which housed the accounts section, or to give it its full title, the London Station Accounts Section (LSA). In addition, the adjacent Arundel House, since 1941, had provided a counter

(Arundel House acceptance office counter, April 1952)

acceptance office for customers wishing to write out and hand in their telegrams in person and for messengers from private companies and other organisations to hand deliver them for onward transmission overseas. The counter office was staffed by P&TOs, or Postal and Telegraph Officers and the grade was operative from 1946 until 1972, when they were re-designated Postal Officers. In addition, Arundel House was linked via its basement to Electra House, and provided subterranean locker facilities for the staff, together with office facilities, and with rooms on upper floors used for recruitment of operators.

The lower ground floor of Electra House provided the staff entrance on the west of the building, down a slope from Arundel Street, through double doors, with access to two lifts manned by uniformed gentlemen in brown livery. No doubt a throwback to former and grander days, they were sadly made redundant by the late 1960s as the lifts were automated. The lower ground floor was also home to the refectory, where one had the option to queue up for service with a tray, or to use the waitress service, albeit at a premium. Food and drink were available from the large kitchens and the coffee lounge virtually 24 hours a day. There was also a well frequented licensed bar with its own cellar, located at the opposite end of the refectory.

The upper ground floor housed the Local Room, which primarily handled UK traffic. By the 1960s it ranged from Zone 10 (TAS Forwarding) to Zone 15 (Telex Forwarding). The TAS system (Teleprinter Automatic Switching) linked Electra House with London and provincial branch offices at larger post offices, whilst the telex system was to facilitate receipt and delivery of overseas telegrams directly to and from commercial subscribers' offices. The Teleprinter Concentrator Position (TCP) was also located in the Local Room. These machines were connected by direct lines to major telegram subscribers including banks and government departments including MOD Boddington, in Dorset, now home to the tank museum.

The Issue Department, processing telegrams for delivery in London by messenger, occupied the north-east corner of the room and the Phone Room, which transferred by the late 1950s to the second floor to make way for expansion of other departments, was originally situated in the middle of the room. Despite being partitioned off, it can have hardly been ideal for the Phone Room to share the room with instruments generating considerably high noise levels at peak times. As early as 1949 it was estimated that the Phone Room would handle up to 5,000 messages a day, all of which would have contributed to the high daily decibel rating.

(Local Room, Teleprinter Concentrator Position, 1950)

The Local Room was also to be the location of the 'Details' desk where operators could check on the availability of overtime, which over the years there was generally no shortage of.

The Local Room also housed Lamson vacuum tube systems, one connected to the Services Department on the sixth floor whereby service messages relating to telegrams could be speedily transported, whilst another was connected to the offices of the Great Northern Telegraph Company, situated at Bishopsgate in the City of London. A further such system linked the counter office in Arundel House to the Issue Department in the Local Room, from where telegrams received over the counter could be expedited to the relevant circuits for onward transmission.

Room Two on the first floor housed the Great Northern circuits in Zone 21, linking to Scandinavian destinations. The Great Northern Telegraph Company (GN) started life as the Danish-Norwegian Telegraph Company in 1868 with subsequent links on to Sweden and Russia. It won the contract in 1870 to lay cables from Russia to Japan, China and Hong Kong and an early

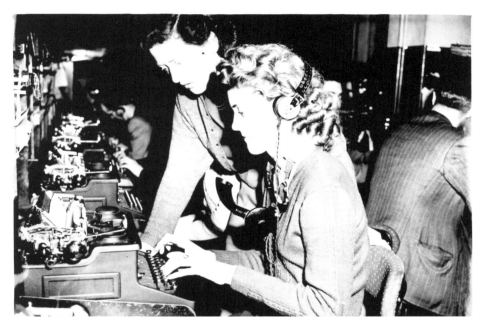

(Miss W. Brocklesby and Miss R. E. Ward, Phonogram Room, May 1953)

letterheading listed their offices in Denmark, Norway, Sweden, Russia, China, Manila, Japan, etc. In more recent times GN collaborated with the British Post Office to complete the eastern part of the SCOTICECAN cable running from Scotland to Thorshavn in the Faroe Islands and on to Reykjavik in Iceland. The cable continued on to Greenland and then to Newfoundland. The Scotland-to-Thorshavn section was 50% owned by the Post Office and 25% each by GN and the Danish PTT service, and the Thorshavn to Iceland section owned 12½% by the Danish PTT, with GN owning the rest.

Zone 22 contained African circuits to Lagos, Lusaka, Cape Town and Johannesburg. Zones 23 and 24 connected to Barbados, Montreal, Sydney, Tel Aviv and Accra in Ghana. Zones 25 and 26 housed circuits to Bombay, Calcutta, Dacca, Cairo, Khartoum, Tehran, Damascus plus Madrid and Bilbao. These latter two circuits might carry messages marked '*Via Entel*' which referred to the Spanish national telecommunications company established in 1961 and operating for the next decade. Other earlier specific route designations were '*Via Belgo-Imperial*' to Belgium and 'Via Radio Athens'to Greece.

(Receiving on the Accra, Ghana wireless circuit, June 1951)

Room Two was also home to TAS receiving circuits and connections to the main Provincial telegraph offices on Zones 27 and 28. The TAS Network had first been mooted in 1935 as a means to enable UK telegraph offices and larger post offices to connect to each other through a simple trunk dialling system. The decision was made in 1937 to go ahead with experiments and tests on such a system, only to be suspended upon the outbreak of the Second World War. After the war, work on the system recommenced but it wasn't until 1949 that it came into operation. The system facilitated the receipt of telegrams on gummed tape from UK telegraph offices for onward transmission overseas via Electra House. As with messages received from overseas circuits, the tape was fed from the teleprinter through a stout brass box, known commonly as a gum pot, containing water to moisten the tape, before being cut and laid out on a telegram message form, the tape being drawn from right to left, generally by the tip of a pair of scissors before being placed on the message form. The system was not particularly sympathetic to left-handed operators. Gum pots measured 5¾ x 3¾ inches and 2¾ high and weighing in at 3½ pounds. In the 1940s and 1950s internal messengers would have the responsibility of making sure the gum pots were topped up with water and kept clean. A prominent maker of that period was Cable and General Instruments who were situated at Beckenham in Kent.

Messages having been gummed on to the appropriate message form were then scrutinised to ensure they contained the correct number of words and all figures or unusual words, which were collated at the bottom of the form, were checked before the message was timed and date-stamped on a Blick time stamp machine. They were then released into the system, being carried away on the extensive rubber belt system, perhaps destined to travel hundreds of yards across the building and up to another floor to the requisite outgoing overseas

(Transmitting to Bombay, November 1950)

(Transmitting to Wellington, New Zealand, mid 1950s. Note the paper cone on a receiver to amplify the audio Morse signal)

circuit. Any discrepancies, especially between the text and the collated figures at the end of the message would necessitate the sending of a service message to the originating office or Office of Origin, to clarify matters.

The Blick Time Recorder Company had a long history of supplying products such as 'clocking in' machines used at factories and offices, and in 1993 was to buy the Time and Security business from Mercury Communications, then owned by Cable and Wireless.

Room Two was one of the key instrument rooms, which along with the second and third floors housed the many overseas circuits. One can imagine the noise level during a busy period with perhaps hundreds of teleprinters, transmitters and perforator keyboards operating at the same time in a space perhaps 160 feet long by 100 feet wide. Yet operators soon accepted the noise levels as the norm and they rarely seemed to affect peoples' concentration.

The Inward Press Office (IPO) was also situated in Room Two. It handled all press traffic received from overseas for UK delivery, whether by telex, tied line, telephone or by hand delivery.

The Outward Press Office (OPO) in Room Two facilitated and prioritised the handling and onward transmission of press telegrams which generally had limited currency. These were received from newspapers and news agencies in the UK such as The Associated Press, Reuters and the Press Association (PA) along with the various foreign national agencies such as TASS, the Soviet news agency. The messages were given a certain priority, despite the rate paid generally being half that of full-rate telegrams, and often press messages would be taken by hand to the requisite outgoing circuit to avoid any chance of delay with using the regular belt system which could be prone to snarl-ups. Also bearing in mind that many press messages were of considerable length, a hank of 5-unit tape accompanying a message to be re-transmitted was always appreciated on the out-going circuit.

Just outside Room Two was the Details Office for signing on at the beginning of a shift and to check on the availability of overtime. Many a tardy employee rushed to sign on before the 'signing-on' cards were withdrawn, necessitating the filling in of the 'Late Book' with an appropriate excuse, some more inventive than others. Assuming one's surname was located towards the end of the alphabet, Zacsinsky for example, and that the details officer worked through the cards from A to Z, one might gain precious seconds in managing to sign on 'in time'.

Room Three, on the second floor, contained circuits to Hamburg and some Gentex circuits on Zones 31 and 33, with further circuits on Zones 43 and 45 on the third floor. Gentex was a contraction of General European Network of Telex Exchanges and the system allowed the operator in London to dial directly to certain European countries, and to send a telegram to the nearest relevant office for the addressee. That office would effect delivery, as appropriate, by telephone and/or by messenger.

Also housed in Room Three were circuits to the U.S.A. connecting to RCA New York, Commercial Radio, Mackay Radio and Western Union. In addition that floor also housed an odd assortment of circuits to destinations such as Berne, Moscow and Kinshasa in Zaire.

Adjoining Room Three on the second floor was the re-located Phonogram Room or Phone Room as it was popularly known. It was primarily staffed by OTO2s who would receive Phonograms, or telegrams received by telephone, from customers who had dialled in on 557 (or 559 for Overseas Telegram Enquiries). Operators would type the in-coming telegrams onto message forms, whilst sitting at positions on long extended tables, plugging in their headphones to accept incoming calls. In addition, other operators would call subscribers to read out out-going telegrams over the telephone in a separate area of the Phone Room.

Payment for Phonograms was generally made via account facilities set up for commercial organisations, although telephone subscribers could also pay via their 'phone bills. Payment could also be made by inserting coins in a telephone box, the operator recognising the amount of money paid by the sounds the different coins made when inserted.

In a small adjacent 'annex' at right angles to the main acceptance suite was the TTO (880 on the telephone dial) with plug and socket switchboards

(Transmitting to New York on the Mackay Radio circuit, April 1952)

*(Mr. R. J. Mason pictured at a 'scrutinising and acceptance check point',
the Inward Received Check (IRC), which connected to the belt system for
internal message distribution)*

(Electra House Phonogram Room receiving positions, 1st January 1958)

connecting to commercial subscribers. Urgent telegrams with stock market prices perhaps from the Paris Bourse, or commodity prices from Johannesburg and exotic destinations such as Phuket, in Thailand were swiftly dealt with there on a regular basis.

The Phone Room was also home to the two large leather-bound volumes of the 'Berne List' which in those pre-Internet days listed just about every destination in the world where one could send a telegram to. It would be especially important to check carefully with customers over destinations with common names such as Springfield in the U.S.A. for example, there being many towns of that name in many different states. The Berne List was compiled by the ITU (The International Telegraph Union), based at Berne in Switzerland. It was founded in 1865 and is the oldest of the United Nations agencies, adopted as such in 1947.

Operators needed to be wary of unusual addresses and an unsuspecting new recruit might well be caught unawares when taking down a telegram to 'Salisbury Road, Esher' rather than 'Salisbury, Rhodesia'. This gaffe proved possible as the occasional inland telegram did find its way into the system, and a misheard wording on a poor telephone line could perhaps direct a message to the 'House of Swedish Passions', rather than 'Swedish Fashions'. A book recording some of the more interesting gaffes was kept in the Phone Room.

(Phonogram Room, February 1965, featuring Mr. Vic Hord, centre left)

Also occupying space on the second floor were the ill-fated chapel, situated above the main entrance to the building, and the Pay Office, at the eastern extremity of the building, visited by most staff on Fridays for their weekly wages paid in cash. The Pay Office could also be described as ill-fated, after a robbery left terrified staff bound and gagged whilst the thieves made their getaway, allegedly with a £27,000 haul. Nobody was ever caught or prosecuted for the crime.

Room Four on the third floor contained middle-eastern morse circuits on Zone 41 connecting to Kuwait, Bahrain, Baghdad, Kabul plus Addis Ababa and Asmara then in Ethiopia, and Dar es Salaam in East Africa. It also had connections to Vatican City, Bucharest, Sofia and Warsaw. Zone 42 contained the historic South American cable circuits to Rio, Buenos Aires, or 'Baires' as it was commonly referred to and others, as well as Port Stanley in the Falklands. Freetown in Sierra Leone was also accommodated there.

Morse slip had been in use for many years, with its holes representing dots and dashes being punched above and below the central sprocket line of the tape. In addition, experienced operators were able to transcribe a message by reading the wavy lines printed by a Siphon Recorder onto a blank paper tape.

(A 1920s model of a Siphon Recorder)

This device, working on a similar principle to a modern ink-jet printer, was invented by Lord Kelvin in 1867. It used an undulator with a stylus fed with ink via a fine glass siphon, and an experienced operator could read and transcribe the content of the message received. It provided a permanent record of messages and was useful where an incoming Morse signal was weak or distorted, mostly those received from certain South American cable stations. The method of transcribing from the tape was known as TRS, or Typing Running Slip. The paper tape was fed into a frame positioned across the front

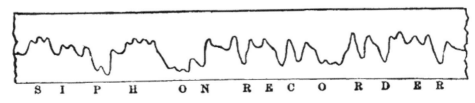

(Audio Morse, undulator reception and Typing Running Slip, April 1952)

of a typewriter from right to left as the operator typed the incoming message onto a telegram form. The operator controlled the speed of the process with pressure from their left knee.

The final wireless circuits at Electra House to use Morse were Asmara and Addis Ababa in Ethiopia, Baghdad in Iraq, Bahrain and last of all by the end of the 1960s, was Kabul in Afghanistan.

Still in Room Four, Zone 43 housed TAS receivers, Zone 44 circuits to Mediterranean destinations such as Milan, Tripoli in Libya, Gibraltar, Rome and Malta, together with Lisbon. The list of circuits on that floor was completed by some Gentex ones.

The fourth floor housed the main engineering workshops, with other smaller repair facilities sited strategically on other floors, close to working telegraph circuits.

The fifth floor had in the early days been mostly the preserve of the Marconi Company. It housed amongst other things the Picture Room, which was home to the substantial facsimile equipment, which was the forerunner of the modern fax machine. It was used primarily for sending and receiving press photographs from around the world, although a 'hard' copy of an important document or contract could also be sent in that way. The wireless fax machine had been invented by Richard H. Ranger in 1924 for the RCA company in America and a photograph of the then U.S. president, Calvin Coolidge, became the first photographic image sent successfully by 'trans-oceanic radio facsimile' in November of that year.

A picture for transmission would be clamped to a slowly spinning drum and scanned as it revolved. The impulses containing the image would be transmitted to its destination where a similar revolving cylinder, with a sheet of photographic film attached, would receive it. The drum would be removed to a 'dark room' for the film to be developed in the ordinary way with a print being made on photographic paper. Facsimile machines emitted a curious undulating 'whine', which varied from a low to a high pitch. This noise

(Muirhead monochrome facsimile transmitter, early 1950s)

represented an amplified record of the transmission, and it could be used to check the successful transmission of the picture. The whole process of sending one image would take about ten minutes.

The commercial value of the system was immediately obvious especially to the newspaper industry but also to the wider world of commerce where copies of urgent documents could be transmitted quickly and easily. The first colour 'photo-telegram' was sent in January 1946 from the Picture Room in Electra House to Australia. It was a four-colour, half-tone picture.

In the pre-National Health Service days of the 1930s and 1940s, Electra House boasted its own resident doctor, nurse and dentist, housed in a small suite of rooms in the south-western corner of the fifth floor, the dentist operating his drills by using a treadle. Injections against tropical diseases for staff going overseas were also either arranged there or at the London School

(A considerably scaled down facsimile machine, pictured in 1957)

of Tropical Medicine, now the London School of Hygiene and Tropical Medicine, which is situated at Gower Street in Central London and is part of the University of London. There was even a visiting chiropodist available to staff. In addition there was a resident Welfare Officer. These facilities no doubt reflected the social-mindedness and forward thinking of Sir Edward Wilshaw. They also would have cut down on staff absences when minor medical or dental treatment was required and with over 3,000 staff on the payroll it was extremely useful to have in-house medical facilities available in case of emergencies.

Another example of Sir Edward's generosity to benefit the staff was a fund, 'The Edward Wilshaw Trust', which was announced in November 1940, whereby he donated £52,000 to set it up, to benefit staff and their dependents in need of financial help. His gesture was also to encourage generous donations to the fund from staff stationed at the company's 129 offices plus its cable ships and of course from staff at Electra House itself. The fund would continue to benefit employees, their widows and their dependents for many years to come.

In that post-war period, telegrams could be filed by private customers in person at Cable and Wireless offices or larger Post Offices, which would send them on to Electra House by teleprinter or telephone, or they could hand them in at the Arundel House counter in person. Companies would hand deliver them to a counter office. 'phone them in, or in later times, send them in by telex or even private line. Once in the system the telegram would be routed to its outgoing circuit for onward transmission. Once sent, the message would be timed and dated and signed or stamped with the sending operator's initials. From there it would be in the hands of the Forward Revision who would file it in a pad. 'Padding Up' was done by OTO2s and was a necessary, but to some, boring job. The day's traffic would then be bagged up and sent to the LSA for accounting purposes. Telegrams transiting London would be received, checked, timed and released into the system to be sent via the belt system to the relevant outgoing circuit.

Telegrams received from all parts of the globe for UK addresses would be directed to the relevant department for delivery, be it by hand by messenger, by telephone, TAS or telex. Copies of these messages would be collected for filing by OTO2s and taken to Received Revision on the sixth floor of the building for 'padding up'.

After the end of the Second World War the sixth floor was home to the London Training School, which had been sent there in 1941 after the transfer of staff and facilities from the wrecked Moorgate building, with a variety of smaller offices housing the Engineer-in-Chief, a laboratory, a workshop, and a further suite of offices occupied by the Marconi Company. Eventually, in time, after the nationalisation of Cable and Wireless its employees training was completed at Porthcurno and under the Post Office, training of operators took place primarily at Government Buildings, Bromyard Avenue, Acton, and the sixth floor space was to be used by the Received Revision and the Main Services departments. As the name implies Received Revision dealt primarily with handling copies of telegrams received, collecting them from the various circuits around the building and sorting (Collect and Sort) then filing them alpha numerically (Padding Up), before their transfer to the Accounts Department for charging purposes, and eventually for storage. The Services Department was primarily concerned with queries relating to telegrams.

The other two ancillary departments were Forward Revision, with stations on different floors dealing with filing copies of traffic sent overseas, and the Issue Department, located on the Upper Ground floor. Issue was primarily concerned with facilitating delivery instructions via Adrema metal plate positions, and the copying of messages for accounting and reference purposes. The Adrema system used small metal plates measuring 10 x 4 cm., containing raised lettering with delivery instructions relating to a particular telegraphic address. The telegram was laid flat and the metal plate inserted into a hinged machine which stamped out an impression of the relevant instructions. The system was similar to the now virtually defunct method of running a credit card through a machine to make an impression on a processing slip. The Adrema Company was based in Berlin and the name was taken from the contraction of the word Adressenmachine.

Also situated in the Issue Department was the Bad Names Office (BNO) where faulty addresses on telegrams could be sent to try to identify them correctly. If a corrupted Registered Telegraphic Address (RTA) was received, an experienced Bad Names Officer might instantly identify the addressee, perhaps recognising regular traffic to a customer from a particular business subscriber, or perhaps by spotting and correcting just one errant letter in the address. If there was a good chance that the correct addressee had been identified but without a certain identification, the telegram could be sent out as a 'try' message which would give the potential addressee some clues

(Adrema position, Issue Department, 1952)

regarding the message, where it was from and a signature perhaps to help them identify if it was indeed for them. The office of origin of the message would be advised of potential non-delivery via a coded 'OLWAY PAMNO' service message which translated to 'address not registered we try delivery to…'. Should there be no clue to the correct address, or if a potential addressee had rejected the 'try' message, a RAJAJ service message would be sent to the office of origin, advising them of the fact.

The copying of messages by the Issue Department involved the process of laying damp tissue paper on a telegram to make a copy. Unsurprisingly, copies were notoriously variable in quality.

By the 1940s, the seventh, and top floor of Electra House was occupied by the Accounts Department (LSA) and in those days before computers ran our lives the company relied on accounting machines supplied by the Powers-Samas Company, which were by today's standards extremely large and noisy but the best available option of the day. Powers-Samas was owned by the U.S.-based Remington Rand Company, which was competing with IBM for their market share. In the UK this equipment was commonly known as 'Acc and Tab', or Accounting and Tabulating.

The top floor was also at that time the base for the Girl Messengers who delivered internal messages. They were mostly employed as school leavers from 14 years of age and were encouraged to better themselves within the company, and many progressed to other departments, some being trained as OTOs. They were well looked after and even merited their own 'Girls' Lavatory', but woe betide any that attempted to use the 'Ladies Lavatory' across the other side of the seventh floor. A supervisor with responsibility for the well-being, and no doubt moral welfare, of the messengers, who remained long in the memory, was the redoubtable Miss Bucknell who reigned supreme in that post from 1937 to 1948.

Keeping such a large and well-frequented building clean was a monumental task, with its hundreds of machines clattering away at any given time. Machines punching holes in paper tape were bound to throw much dust in the air, whilst the ceaseless progression of employees moving around the building over the twenty-four hours also created more dust and dirt. In addition many people in the history of Electra House were smokers, adding further pollution to the air. It's no surprise that many long-term employees didn't live long after retirement, to reap the benefits. It's perhaps an apocryphal and certainly ironic tale that some employees after a lifetime of earnings, vastly inflated by working excessive amounts of overtime, were able to buy their dream holiday home, a villa in the south of France perhaps, but would never have the time off to enjoy it, and as they might be lucky to reach retirement age might not enjoy it then either.

With the lethal combination of mountains of paper and tape in the building combined with hundreds of people smoking with no restriction, it's a wonder that many a time the whole building didn't go up in smoke.

Luckily, such a catastrophic event did not happen, and some credit must go to the army of cleaners working to keep the building 'spic and span' on a daily basis. In the post-war period, at one time 40 redoubtable British charladies would tackle the monumental task, both day and night. As time moved on their places might be taken by successive waves of immigrants, who started to take on the lower paid 'dirty jobs' that the British no longer felt able to do.

Modern day Health and Safety officers would be appalled at the conditions staff at Electra House experienced, with air and noise pollution ever present, yet nobody seemed to complain and people just 'got on with it', perhaps because they had no choice but also perhaps with a touch of that 'War Time Spirit'.

Nationalisation – From Cable and Wireless to the Post Office

(Electra House at the centre of the world - Great Circle map, 1945)

Following the Labour Party's victory in the 1945 General Election, the new Socialist government, under Prime Minister Clement Attlee, announced its decision in November of that year to nationalise Cable and Wireless Ltd. Sir Edward Wilshaw and the Court of Directors of the company were understandably strongly opposed to the move and did what they could to fight it, and a petition against the *'Cable and Wireless Bill'* was put before Select Committees of both Houses of Parliament. The press lent their support to the company and were unanimous in their praise for the 'exemplary manner in which Cable and Wireless was run' but the protests fell on deaf ears and the Act came into force on 1st January 1947.

In November 1946, as a fine 'leaving present' for Sir Edward, Lord Inverleith on behalf of the Cable and Wireless board presented him with a

7-foot scale model of the *CS Edward Wilshaw,* which was then in the planning stages and was to be launched in 1948. The launch was attended by Sir Edward and Lady Wilshaw, Sir Stanley and Lady Angwin and other dignitaries. The *CS Edward Wilshaw* was built at the renowned Swan, Hunter shipyards on the River Tyne. With a complement of 84 and weighing in at 2,562 tons it was the largest cable-laying and repair ship of its day, giving long and excellent service to the company in the Indian Ocean, Mediterranean and Pacific Ocean, before being scrapped in 1979. The model can currently be seen on display at the telegraph museum at Porthcurno.

(CS Edward Wilshaw with 'naval escorts')

Also in November 1946, Electra House received more august visitors in the shape of Lord and Lady Mountbatten, who came to witness the inauguration of the London to Malta photo-telegraph service. Lord Mountbatten was also there to personally thank 130 staff members who had served in Telcom units in the Far East with groups under his command as Supreme Allied Commander South East Asia Command, a post he had occupied from 1943 till 1946. He shook hands with each and every one of them including one Jack 'Ginger' Pennington, of whom we'll hear more later on. His Lordship, soon to take up his post as the last Viceroy of India, then addressed a packed audience in the staff refectory, congratulating them and the company for their fine war work.

This was not quite the end for Telcom units in conflict areas, as from 1950 to 1955 one was set up in Korea during the Korean War, operating a wireless field unit to facilitate government and press coverage of the conflict, and to enable members of the armed forces to maintain contact with family and friends.

So, on 1st January 1947, Sir Stanley Angwin (1883–1959) took over as Chairman of the newly nationalised part of Cable and Wireless Ltd., to oversee the company's move into the public sector, and the transfer of UK assets to the Post Office. He had a long history of working in engineering and telegraphy bringing his own expertise to a difficult job. He had also had an extremely illustrious First World War military career, serving with a telegraphy unit at Gallipoli, Egypt, Palestine and France. As Colonel Angwin he was awarded the DSO and the MC, and was mentioned in dispatches five times, but you can imagine, like many of his contemporaries, he would be reticent to talk about his war service. He was to continue in the post of Chairman until 1951, when he left to become Chairman of the Commonwealth Telecommunications Board.

With the completion of the nationalisation, Cable and Wireless (Holdings) Ltd, under Sir Edward Wilshaw as Chairman, continued to own all its overseas assets including 155,000 nautical miles of submarine cable, plus a fleet of cable ships and the majority of its overseas cable offices. It would continue to operate telecommunication services outside the UK and in addition, within the UK it would retain ownership of the Porthcurno telegraph station, the Plymouth Cable Depot and the Exiles Club at Twickenham, Middlesex.

All other UK assets were then integrated into those of the Post Office and on 1st April 1950 all UK operating staff, some 3,500 men and women, with the exception of those employed at Porthcurno, were transferred to Post Office Cable and Wireless Ltd.

The harsh winter weather of early 1947 also brought severe problems to London Station. The winter, the coldest for many years, brought fuel shortages and power cuts to much of the country with the consequent disruption to road and rail travel, as at times many roads became impassable due to excessive snow and ice. Coal and oil supplies were still depleted from the war, but luckily, with its own electricity generator, Electra House fared better than most companies in dealing with the situation, but many employees found it difficult or impossible to get to work at times due to the conditions. The severe weather continued until March, with yet more problems to follow as floods followed a thaw.

1947 was proving to be quite a memorable and eventful year for the company, and to add a little 'light relief' Electra House was visited on Empire Day, 24th May, by the BBC with a two-part television broadcast hosted by popular broadcaster Freddie Grisewood. The programme covered live picture transmissions to and from Cape Town and he exchanged greetings with the mayor of that city by radio-telephone. Grisewood's claim to fame was that he had presented the BBC's very first outside broadcast, in 1937, covering the wedding of King George VI to Queen Elizabeth, the future Queen Mother. He went on, a year later, to host *What's My Line?* a popular BBC radio 'panel' game, which ran until 1967.

Also in 1947, on 1st October, as the London Telecommunications Region of the Post Office struggled to cope with the extra work load, the External Telecommunications Executive (ETE) was set up to run all ex-Cable and Wireless Services in the UK, including the Post Office's own Overseas Telegraph Department, on a day-to-day basis.

The overseas Cable and Wireless employees continued to run the far-flung stations around the globe and Cable and Wireless started to plough its own path as the company began to explore and develop new technologies especially in the worlds of satellite communications and telephony, eventually with its Mercury Communications company. They would look towards Porthcurno as their UK home station where the training school for operators and engineers had been founded in 1915 and was maintained as such until 1993.

A typical training course for new Cable and Wireless recruits in the post-war period included a nine month sojourn at Electra House where instruction was given on the theory and practical application of electricity and magnetism, and on mathematics. In addition they were taught the skills required for operating circuits as well as instrument maintenance. After this period they were transferred to Porthcurno for a similar time span to receive specialised tuition in submarine cable engineering. Following this 18 month training period the student would be sent to an overseas station such as Gibraltar or Carcavelos for hands-on experience. Having passed satisfactorily through all the stages of training and having passed the relevant exams, the recruit would then be liable for transfer at short notice to just about anywhere in the world, with further advancement to higher grades possible through passing further exams. At many overseas stations telegraph operators were recruited locally.

Many employees would visit the Exiles Club at Meadowbank, a large modern rectangular building, bought by the Eastern Telegraph Company in

1920. It was situated in Orleans Park at St. Margarets, Twickenham and when on home leave, or furlough as it was known, the spacious grounds offered facilities for an extensive range of sports such as rugby, football, cricket and hockey, with a putting green and perhaps the odd gymkhana thrown in for good measure. It was also a very good social venue to renew old acquaintances and make new friends within the company. The facilities had been in continual use, even during wartime, and were not to escape enemy action when the bowling green was hit by incendiary bombs in 1941, to the great indignation of ground staff and employees alike. The Exiles Club was to continue providing a venue for reunions until the premises were sold in early 1999.

1948 saw London host the first post-war summer Olympics and talented Scottish runner and Electra House staff member Alexander (Alick) Pirie (1901-1975) was given the honour of carrying the Olympic Torch through Reigate, Surrey, on its way to Wembley stadium. He was accompanied by his 17 year-old son, Gordon (1931-1991), who was to go on, in the 1950s, to have an illustrious career as one of the world's leading distance runners, at one time holding world records in the men's 3,000 and 5,000 metres track events.

Sadly, Alick was to die, of natural causes, whilst working on duty at Cardinal House. He was, apparently, one of a select group of employees working in 'The Clearing House', a top secret office on the sixth floor, where batches of telegrams from the previous day's traffic were examined for 'security purposes'. As the office did not officially exist, it was no surprise that Prime Minister Harold Wilson, had previously 'reacted with fury' when faced with a February 1967 *Daily Express* article by senior journalist Chapman Pincher, that claimed that the process had been in practice for some years. Pincher stated that 'thousands of private cables and telegrams sent out from Britain by the Post Office or from commercial cable companies are regularly being made available to the security authorities for scrutiny'. Pincher's source was named as a Robert Lawson who had previously worked for Western Union and the Commercial Cable Company. The whole episode left Wilson with a considerable amount of egg on his face!

The exact location of Alick's death was not revealed and he was reported to have died in the corridor outside the office, which the police when investigating, were not allowed access to, no doubt for 'security reasons'. Some of the events may be apocryphal but they were reported by a credible source.

Another talented distance runner on the track and in cross-country events was Jack 'Ginger' Pennington, an engineer, who joined Cable and Wireless in 1946, after war service in Burma under Lord Mountbatten. Jack, the grandson of Percy Pennington, who had retired from Cable and Wireless in 1933, was always ready to represent the company, and later, after nationalisation, the Civil Service, in athletics matches against university teams and other leading opponents. He was a leading light in the founding of the Cable and Wireless Sports and Social Club, which was established in 1947. He was to leave the company in 1958, emigrating with his family to Australia, where he had a long and illustrious career as a runner, athletics coach and founder of running clubs in Canberra. In later life, he put pen to paper and wrote his autobiography, the aptly-titled *A Life On The Run.* Jack led a fit and active life in retirement, right up to his death aged 93, in October 2016.

(Receiving from Paris, December 1950)

As the world continued to pick up the pieces after the war, with business and personal contacts being re-established around the globe, Cable and Wireless was riding on the crest of the wave of the increased international commercial activity. It is worth noting that by 1949 Cable and Wireless employed around 13,300 men and women comprising 57 different nationalities, working in 166 stations and offices in some 70 countries around the world. In addition to the traditional telegraph circuits there were at that time 21 photo-telegraph circuits in operation. In addition the company owned a fleet of eight cable ships to maintain the submarine cable network. By 1950 Electra House was handling 15 million telegrams a year, 6 million originating in the UK, 5.75 million received from overseas for UK delivery, and 3.25 million messages in transit via London. In addition, the Central Telegraph Office at St. Martin's Le Grand in the same period handled 4.2 million overseas telegrams via its own links.

In 1951 the Festival of Britain was held from May to September, on a 27-acre site on the south bank of the Thames, and was officially opened by King George VI on 3rd May. It provided the excuse for the first full illuminations in London since the end of the war, transforming the river and its environs at night, all of which was warmly welcomed by Londoners, still surrounded by the drabness of austerity. It showcased Britain's leading role at the cutting edge of new technology in the new post-war world, and it proved very popular with the public, with some 8 million paying visitors during that time. It famously featured the Skylon Tower, a futuristic needle-shaped structure cleverly designed to appear to be floating in the air, with no visible means of support, much like the British economy at the time, it was suggested. The site also housed the Royal Festival Hall, the only substantial legacy of the Festival to survive to the present day, and the Dome of Discovery, the largest dome in the world at the time.

Cable and Wireless was represented in the Dome of Discovery by the Dome Colonial Telegraph Station, a very popular working cable circuit with connections via Electra House to Aden, Accra in Ghana, Ascension, Barbados, Cyprus and Nairobi in Kenya. Visitors were encouraged to send questions to operators in those far distant lands, some queries more serious than others, with some young ladies keen to know if the operators might be "tall, dark and handsome", or "if they were married"! During the five months of its operation, the temporary station sent over 38,000 messages from the exhibition.

1951 was proving an eventful year for Electra House and telegraphy in general. Even the Pope, Pius XII, with a long-standing interest in telegraphy, got in on the act by proclaiming the Archangel Gabriel the patron saint of telegraphists and telephonists. It is assumed that the archangel's track record of bringing urgent news to the Virgin Mary of her pregnancy made him the 'best man for the job'.

The same year was to see a change of leadership of the nationalised Cable and Wireless Company when Sir Stanley Angwin stepped down, to be replaced by Major-General L. B. Nicholls in March of that year. In recognition of his distinguished service with the company, Sir Stanley was given the honour of having a cable ship named after him. The *CS Stanley Angwin*, based for much of its career in Singapore, was to be built by Swan, Hunter in 1952 and served Cable and Wireless for twenty years, before being sold off for scrap.

One of Major-General Nicholls' first acts as Chairman was to invite Sir Winston Churchill, the then Prime Minister, to a special showing of the recently filmed *Voices Under The Sea*, a documentary primarily about cable laying and shot at sea on the *CS Norseman*, with other scenes shot at Electra House and at Porthcurno.

Two years later in 1953 at a cabinet meeting at 10 Downing Street, the subject of a rise in 'Overseas Telegraph Rates' was discussed. Sir Winston Churchill was told by the Post-Master General (PMG) that these rates yielded £2m per year and despite costs having risen considerably in recent years, there had been no rate rises since 1929. He was further informed "that even at one shilling per word the transatlantic rate will be 4½d (four pence halfpenny) less than the rate charged from the U.S." and "we would be heavily pressed if rates don't rise". Churchill did not support any rises at the time and stated he wished the failure of the nationalisation of Cable and Wireless by "the Socialists" to be seen as a mistake first. The PMG also stated, that "U.S. companies were doing 80% of the transatlantic business and were operating at a loss because of rates we force them to charge", highlighting the supremacy Britain held at the time. He further stated that a new transatlantic cable was being laid in the coming year, which would increase capacity by 15%.

1953 also saw the appointment of H. J. Wellington in the newly instituted post of Telegraph Manager at Electra House. Sadly it was a position he was to hold for just one year until his death in 1954. He was succeeded in July of that year by Mr. H. E. Chapman, a post he was to hold until 1959.

In May 1954 the Electra House chapel, which was designed by Frank Hicks, was finally restored, ten years after its war time damage, and on 1st May it was officially re-dedicated by no less a personage than Dr. Geoffrey Fisher, the Archbishop of Canterbury, who just one year earlier had officiated at the coronation of Queen Elizabeth II, placing King Edward's crown upon her head. He had also performed the wedding ceremony in November 1947 when she had married Prince Philip. Also attending the dedication were the Postmaster-General Earl De La Warr, Sir Edward Wilshaw, at that time the Governor of Cable and Wireless (Holding) Limited, Major-General Nicholls and Lord Pender.

After the ceremony Dr. Fisher was given a guided tour of Room Two and exchanged fraternal greetings via the Singapore circuit with the Bishop of that see.

(The restored inter-denominational chapel)

Sir Edward was to maintain his links to the company until his death in London in 1968, his chauffeur-driven Rolls-Royce with its distinctive number plate NEW 88, being a common sight, parked outside of Electra House well into the 1960s. He had given most of his life to serving the company in one capacity or another, joining in 1894 as a junior and reaching the pinnacle of his career as Managing Director and Chairman, guiding the company through crucial times in the mid-20th century, and latterly as an elder statesman. In all, an involvement lasting an amazing 74 years!

A year later, in November 1955, Cable and Wireless Ltd. finally moved out of Electra House into its new headquarters at Mercury House in Theobald's Road in London W1, which were officially opened by Lord Reith, the erstwhile Director General of the BBC, and for a short period during the Second World War, a director of Cable and Wireless. This left the Post Office External Telecommunications Executive and Cable and Wireless (Holding) Ltd, the investment trust, as sole occupiers of the Victoria Embankment building.

1956 brought a splash of colour to Post Office Cable and Wireless Services in the shape of a bright red 27-foot long, 6-ton mobile telegraph office built on a coach chassis which was used primarily for covering sporting events. Commissioned in April of that year and built by Harrington's of Hove in East Sussex, it had an aluminium body with a 2-stroke Commer diesel engine on a Commer chassis. It would follow major sporting events such as Australian and South African cricket tours of the U.K, International rugby tours and other prime sporting fixtures such as the Open Golf Championships, providing teleprinter and facsimile links to Electra House to convey eagerly awaited press coverage and pictures of the action around the world.

Painted in 'Post Office Red' with 'POST OFFICE CABLE AND WIRELESS SERVICES' emblazoned on the side in gold lettering, and with bumpers and trim also highlighted in gold, it was an eye-catching sight wherever it went. It was 'launched' from King Edward Buildings, the then headquarters of the GPO in the City, by Dr. Charles Hill, later Lord Hill, the Post-Master General, and its first assignment was to cover the Australian cricket tour of that year, transmitting an estimated 1½ million words from various venues back to Electra House for onward transmission. In those early days the bus offered only a point-to-point service to Electra House, but as the technology became available in subsequent years, an international telex service was added connecting to most parts of the world, along with picture services to inland and overseas destinations.

Initially based at Wembley, it was staffed by two engineers and two operators, who could be supplemented by local staff when necessary, with the role of driver performed by one of the engineers. The system would handle transmission of up to 80,000 words a day in press telegrams during Test

(The Mobile telegraph office, restored to its former livery)

matches and operators would be working late into the evening, clearing the mountain of copy, before perhaps starting again the following day. The bus would attract many famous visitors over the years, from stars of the cricket firmament such as Learie Constantine, Keith Miller and Ritchie Benaud to golfer Henry Cotton and the likes of John Arlott the peerless cricket commentator.

Its internal layout comprised an acceptance counter, via the rear entrance with a small rear washroom compartment and a tiny 'quiet room' housing a telephone (used on occasion by Messrs Arlott and his colleagues for placing bets on horse races).

After some 90,000 miles on the road, in 1970, the bus was given a new coat of paint, described as 'telecommunications yellow', along with a complete refit of the interior, and a new name along the side – POST OFFICE INTERNATIONAL TELEGRAPH SERVICES. Several new features were added including new ventilation and heating systems, along with fluorescent lighting, installed above the operating positions. With the exception of the picture transmitter, all the telegraph equipment and furniture were replaced.

It was to continue in use until the mid-1970s, but as daily newspapers and news agencies developed their own overseas links by telex and point-to-point teleprinter connections, and overseas telephone lines became more available and affordable, its days were numbered. The bus sports a distinctive number plate, SLO 24, which presumably alludes to the progress of the static bus, rather than the service offered which would have been first class.

The bus subsequently passed through the hands of several owners, including a company of seed merchants based in the north of England, when it was painted blue and white, and a hippy family who lived in it for a time in a Cambridgeshire field. The bus was then recognised for what it was from its unusual number plate by a passing motorist and it was subsequently acquired for renovation. It was restored to its former glory, and to this day can be seen at certain vintage vehicle fairs around the UK resplendent in its splendid original red and gold livery. The fact that the bus has survived the 40 years since its retirement is remarkable, although one incident on a foggy M1 motorway whilst on 'active service' could have led to its early demise when it was involved in a minor collision, as a result of which the driver was prosecuted for 'driving without due care and attention'.

In 1958 the Post Office's Continental telegram radio circuits were transferred to Electra House from the Central Telegraph Office (CTO) in St Martin's Le Grand, close to St. Paul's Cathedral, to be followed in 1960 by the Continental teleprinter circuits, with the Icelandic cable circuit completing the uniting of all overseas telegraph circuits under the one roof on the Victoria Embankment.

1959 saw the appointment of Mr. R. A. Harrison as Telegraph Manager at Electra House. He had entered Post Office service in 1919 as a telegraph messenger boy and was to serve in the top job until retirement in July 1967 after being awarded the Imperial Service Order (ISO). His successor was Mr. V. J. Habberfield.

Edward VII instituted this particular decoration in 1902, to reward 'selected' civil servants at home and abroad upon retirement, after at least 25 years of domestic service or 16 years on overseas service. The ISO is only awarded with the approval of the sovereign.

A year later in early 1960 a report estimated that there were 680 staff vacancies at Electra House and the CTO, but with the proposed introduction of the Gentex system and other technological improvements to the service, the figure could be reduced by 200. A report in March of that year by H. G. Lillicrap of the ETE, stated that "…for some time it had been impossible to recruit anything like the number of staff required, and services had only been maintained by scheduling an excessive amount of overtime, and still leaving uncovered a large number of duties". Barely a month later a staff ban on overtime working at Electra House was introduced due to the failure of management to recognise a new staff association. This resulted in the temporary withdrawal of the reduced price letter-rate telegram service and questions were then asked in the House of Lords on 30th May 1960 by Lord MacPherson of Drumochter. Lord Chesham in response stated that "the overtime ban had now ended and once the backlog of traffic had been dealt with, the letter rate would be reinstated".

Six weeks later the Postmaster-General Reginald Bevins was asked to make a statement in the House on the staff shortage at Electra House. He replied that "The recruitment position is now encouraging" and that he had "arranged for the level of pay at recruitment level to be increased" and further that he had "shortened the duration of training courses" and was "pressing on more rapidly with mechanisation". For many years large amounts of overtime were available to cover for staff shortages and this enabled operators to boost their basic earnings considerably from a relatively low level when compared to those paid in the commercial world. If one were willing to work 'all the hours under the sun' one could double the weekly wage that way.

Two years later in 1962 the Post-Master General was asked in the House of Commons what proposals he had for overcoming delays being experienced on delivery of telegrams from overseas. He replied "there were 330 vacancies at Electra House with 400 new recruits in training, from a full operational staff of 2,900". He apologised and "hoped that as more staff were trained and gained experience there should be a 'steady improvement'." He also claimed that it took 'several months' to train an overseas telegraph operator.

This was a strange claim to make as trainee OTO2s at that time, after an initial induction course at Government Buildings in Bromyard Avenue, Acton, lasting two weeks, worked at Electra House on primarily clerical duties for some months before returning to Acton for the nineteen week 'Phone Course' whereby operators were taught to touch-type on three-bank Imperial 66 typewriters. (Some years earlier, premises at Bainbridge Street, close to Tottenham Court Road had been used for this training course). Perhaps a year after the 'Phone Course' had been completed, trainees were sent back to Acton for the 12-week-long 'Telex Course'. The telex machines, products of the Creed Company, were similarly fitted with three-bank keyboards. All this meant that it took a few years to fully train an OTO2 and at least five years before completion of the OTO1 training schedule once one had risen up the seniority list and space became available on the 'One's Course'. In fact it was reckoned that of those five years anything up to one whole year could be spent on training, either in the classroom or *in situ*.

An OTO in the post-war period would be allotted their own personal rubber stamp bearing their unique registered initials or lettering, as well as an ink pad, so that every telegram they sent and subsequently stamped could be easily identified should any query arise due to a serious typing error or perhaps in the event of non delivery of the telegram. In addition, all operators needed access to scissors for cutting gummed tape when attaching it to a message

(Gentex section, June 1962)

THE WORLD COULD BE AT YOUR FINGERTIPS

WE ARE LOOKING FOR MALE AND FEMALE STAFF WHO:—

wish to play a vital part in operating the telegraphic network linking this country with the rest of the world,

are seeking an interesting and rewarding career,

have acquired a sound education and can speak clearly on the telephone,

are between 15 and 35 (or, if older than this, have acquired teleprinter or touch-typing experience).

THOSE SELECTED CAN EXPECT:—

full training with pay,

starting pay up to £13.7.6 p.w., according to age,

regular increases to £14.11.6 p.w.,

overtime opportunities,

excellent opportunities for rapid advancement to posts carrying a salary maximum of £981 p.a. and good prospects of promotion to senior posts,

a permanent Civil Service appointment,

a free pension scheme,

very good holidays.

FOR FURTHER DETAILS:— Write, call or phone
**CAREERS DEPARTMENT,
POST OFFICE CABLE AND WIRELESS SERVICES
ARUNDEL HOUSE, 13/15, ARUNDEL ST., W.C.2
TEM 1222 Ex 435**

('The World Could Be At Your Fingertips', Evening News, August 1962)

form, as well as glue to join lengths of perforated 5-unit tape together into a roll when trained as an OTO1. Glue was generally to be housed in a redundant tobacco tin with a hole pierced in the top with a matchstick protruding from the hole.

The Bromyard Avenue facility was to go out of use by 1967, when training was primarily undertaken at Cardinal House at Smithfield in Central London. The construction of Government Buildings had commenced in 1914 for the Ministry of Pensions, but delays due to the First World War meant it was not completed until 1922. Today the buildings have been converted into apartments.

To alleviate the pressure on staff shortages at Electra House and no doubt on the Post-Master General too, an extensive newspaper advertising campaign

(The Discovery, Wellington, President and Chrysanthemum moored off the Victoria Embankment, with Electra House at left, pictured in the 1960s)

was launched in London in the *Evening News and Star* and the *Evening Standard* and in selected provincial dailies. A typical advert proclaimed *"The World Could Be At Your Fingertips"* and it continued, *"We are looking for male and female staff who wish to play a vital part in operating the telegraphic network linking this country with the rest of the world"*. The advert offered amongst other things *"full training with pay, excellent opportunities for rapid advancement, overtime opportunities, a free pension scheme and very good holidays"*.

Efforts were also made to recruit forces personnel who were about to complete their service and re-enter Civvy Street. One magazine *The Communicator*, the 'bible' of the Royal Navy's communications branch, featured full-page adverts offering 'A Career in Telegraphy' in Central London. Recruits were welcome if under 36 years of age, and especially if they already possessed typing and telegraphic skills. Many of those applicants in the 1960s already had typing skills and would also have experience of Morse working which unfortunately was rapidly approaching the end of its useful working life in international telegraphy.

New entrants, after passing a medical examination, started their career as a T/OTO2 (Temporary/Overseas Telegraph Operator 2), rising if they stayed the course to OTO2, by which time they would have been 'established' in a permanent position. Further advancement to OTO1 took place, and after sufficient service, if they were considered suitable material, they would be eligible for promotion to Supervisor. Further advancement was possible for the select few to Assistant Superintendent (A/S, or 'A bar S'), Superintendent and Chief Superintendent. Applicants aged between 15 and 35 who were British subjects or citizens of the Irish Republic were eligible to apply.

At that time technological improvements continued apace as the new Cantat-1 cable was laid to Canada in 1961, followed by the Compac cable two years later, linking western Canada with New Zealand and Australia via Fiji. Both offered many extra circuits for telegraph or telephone use.

By the mid-1960s audio Morse working on the South American (Sams) circuits was being phased out in favour of 5-unit equipment, bringing to an end the long history of operators being trained to read Morse signals. Most Morse keyboards in the earlier days were four-bank against the three-bank 5-unit machines from the later period. 5-unit working had been introduced in the late 1940s and initially there were machines in use to convert 5-unit tapes to Morse ones, and vice versa, but it was a long process and in due course they went out of use.

The Introduction of new automated systems

The Overseas Tape Relay Unit (OTRU), or OverTime Restoration Unit as one wag named it, was installed in 1963 on the seventh floor of Electra House, and officially opened on 13th January 1964, sharing the floor with staff lockers and snooker and table tennis tables. Its first Officer-in-Charge was Mr. J. S. Grant assisted by two Assistant Superintendents, their number later being increased to five. The OTRU was a 'torn-tape' system, whereby an incoming message on 5-unit tape (including a strip with letters and figures printed along the edge) could be torn off and transmitted to a destination in the OTRU system or if not on that system, to be sent downstairs to the relevant outgoing overseas circuit.

(The OTRU system in 1963, ready for it's official opening in January 1964)

The OTRU system represented the first in a series of steps in the increasing use of automation for message handling. As the technology became available it was a logical step to redirect telegrams that were transiting London without the need to retype them, and it represented a considerable saving in time, effort and money, with the predictable eventual reduction in staffing levels. The first three circuits connected to the system were Oslo, Antwerp C/W and Antwerp CTO. Berne followed shortly afterwards only to withdraw from the system a short time later due to the poor 'quality of service' they were receiving, but once certain teething troubles had been ironed out and staff became more competent in using the system, they asked to come back in again.

(OTRU Operator Console, 1963)

Eventually a further twenty-seven overseas circuits were brought into the OTRU together with the Gentex system, seven provincial offices (Belfast, Birmingham, Manchester, Liverpool, Bradford, Bristol and Glasgow), the four London area offices at Broadway, Livonia St., Falcon House and St. Botolph's, as well as connecting it to all the Electra House traffic rooms. The system handled around 20,000 messages a day, or around a quarter of the London Station workload at that time.

By the early 1960s with London's growing commercial expansion, especially in the City of London, it was becoming apparent that Electra House could not cope efficiently with the increased levels of overseas telegrams being handled in the capital and it was decided to open four area offices, or OTAOs – Overseas Telegraphs Area Offices to give them their full title (see *Appendix I*). The target date for opening the first one was 1st January 1962, but it was not until two years later that the plans came to fruition. The first to open was at 1a, Broadway in Westminster in the SW1 postal district in January 1964, followed by Livonia Street in Soho in the West End in W1 in February of that year, Falcon House in the City in EC1 in October 1965, and finally St. Botolph's House at 138-139, Houndsditch at Aldgate also in the City in EC3 in 1967. All offices offered 24-hour coverage.

Messages were received from customers by telephone and telex for onward transmission overseas via Electra House with a steady flow coming the other way for local delivery. Many a disinterested customer would have been telephoned on a Sunday evening at home with an apparently boring and irrelevant message, but that would have been the instruction from his company stored on an Adrema plate, and that's what would have been effected.

Whilst the area offices did not have counter offices for acceptance of telegrams from customers in person, both Broadway and St. Botolph's offices were situated on upper floors of buildings with post offices counters for the public on the ground floor. Acceptance offices for telegrams were however strategically placed around the City of London, notably at the Stock Exchange, at Old Broad Street, at Finsbury House, Finsbury Circus, at Bankside House, Leadenhall, at Cereal House, Mark Lane and at Shorter's Court off Throgmorton Street for the Bank of England. Heathrow Airport also sported two, one in each of the early terminals, Heathrow Central and Heathrow North.

1966 was to bring tragedy to the door of Electra House when the *MV Anzio 1* was lost with all hands in the North Sea on 3rd April. Of its 13 crew, seven were serving or ex-Overseas Telegraph Operators, the other six being family members or friends. The shock felt by family and colleagues when the full facts of the disaster became known, reverberated around the world and to this day, over half a century later, it is still hard to accept by those who were personally affected.

The *MV Anzio 1* was launched in 1903 and was a ship of 216 tons. It was originally named the *Lochinvar* and had spent much of its life working out of Oban on the west coast of Scotland as a Royal Mail steamer, ferrying passengers and mail to Mull and other Western isles. It was eventually sold in 1961 to the Thames and Medway Navigation Co. for service across the Thames Estuary between Southend and Sheerness, in Essex.

In 1964 it was spotted and recognised as the old *Lochinvar* when moored at Tilbury when it was under the ownership of a Squadron-Leader Reginald J. Jones. He agreed to sell it, and the plan evolved to refit the ship and then to sail her to Inverness to run pleasure cruises on inshore waters under the banner 'Cromarty Cruises'. The main partners in the venture were Harry Fotheringham, along with his brother Adam, and Bob Mitchell, who became the ship's engineer. Adam, who was to captain the ship, spent 18 months outfitting the ship, which was ready to sail just prior to Easter 1966.

The ship set sail from Tilbury at 20.30 on Friday 1st April, after receiving a clean bill of health from a Board of Trade surveyor, and with a favourable weather forecast. Overnight the sea was slight with a slow swell as the ship made its way from the Thames Estuary into the English Channel and then the North Sea. On the afternoon of the 2nd, the wind freshened to force 6 and they encountered a rough sea with a heavy swell. By 1600 the wind was at gale force 8 and strengthening, and the captain's last log entry noted his change of course to 'run before wind and sea'.

It's hard to know exactly what happened that night but it seems they were trying to reach the Humber estuary and calmer waters, but were driven towards the shore, running aground with the ship turning on its side. Due to the intensity of the wind and sea state the Humber lifeboat was unable to get close enough to secure a line to the ship and successive attempts to fire a line from the shore fell short. A one-man rescue attempt by Alan Loughton of North Somercoates also failed after he risked his own life in the water to get within hailing distance of the stricken vessel. He urged crew members to jump into the water, realising it might be their only hope of survival, but to no avail and as daylight came and the visibility and conditions improved the rescue services were able to search for survivors. There were no signs of life, and sadly it was just a question of recovering the bodies of the crew.

The crew comprised Harry Fotheringham, Bill Chambers, Danny Cameron, John Gibson, Harry Slinn, Len Smith and Lew Watts, all telegraphists, plus Harry's brother Adam Fotheringham, John MacLardy, Ray Martin, Bob Mitchell, and father and son Alex Mitchell Snr. and Jnr.

The inquest was held on 14th June, at Louth in Lincolnshire and the coroner whilst summarising the evidence, stated that the seaworthiness and stability of the ship were not in question. In addition the crew was experienced and more than capable of handling the ship. It was all a terribly tragic accident, caused by a very strong wind and a very rough sea, which could not have been easily foreseen.

Geoffrey P. Jones, who knew all seven telegraphists personally, wrote a detailed booklet to commemorate the lives of the crew and to publish all the known facts of the tragedy. It was issued in conjunction with an appeal for donations to benefit the ten fatherless children left behind. Donations to the fund came in from all directions, from personal subscriptions, from unions, from Electra House and all the other associated telegraph offices in London and around the country, as well as post and parcel offices including many donations from people who did not know the deceased but were deeply touched by the terrible events. Almost £2,000 was raised and distributed to the dependents of the crew, a considerable sum in 1966. After the fund closed further profits made from the sale of the booklet went to the existing Christmas Fund to provide presents for children of deceased colleagues. This fund was finally wound up in the spring of 1984.

A memorial service conducted by the Rev. G. T. Morphet, from the 'Mission to Seamen', was held in a packed Electra House chapel on 23rd May, followed by an informal tea at Electra House, the first occasion that the five widows of the crew and mothers of the deceased had all met together to comfort each other in their grief.

Cardinal House

(Cardinal House, from Farringdon Road, May 1968)

Cardinal House, which was to became home to the MRC (Message Relay Centre) and TRC (Telegram Re-transmission Centre) automatic message switching centres, was constructed in the early 1960s and was situated opposite

Farringdon Underground station in Cowcross Street, and close to Farringdon Road, on the edge of the Smithfield meat market area. Farringdon Road is the northward continuation of Farringdon Street, the change in the suffix being due to the fact that one has left the City of London, where there are no thoroughfares using the word 'road'.

In 1967 it was to become the home of the SID (Station Instruction Department), the training facility for OTOs, or ITTS (International Telegraph Training School) as it became known, which moved there from Government Buildings, Bromyard Avenue, Acton, in west London. The Inland Telegraph service Training School was also housed next door at Caxton House at one time. In addition, it later was home to the Teleprov training facility for operators handling the wool trade traffic between Australia and UK provincial offices such as Bradford, Manchester and Liverpool.

Caxton House, situated at 2, Farringdon Road, on the corner of Cowcross Street and sharing the building with Cardinal House, served several uses over the years. It housed the LSA backdate Service Deal at one time as well as serving as a storage facility and as office space, and also as home to the Post Office Photographic Unit, which later moved to a building in Old Street. Apart from taking photographs for publicity and other Post Office requirements the department worked with telephone exchanges, as meter readings were at that time photographed for accounting purposes.

Comprising eleven storeys, Cardinal House had several main functions during its use by the Post Office. In its early days the OTO training school occupied the eighth, tenth and eleventh floors, with the MRC and TRC automatic switching systems situated on the first floor and fifth respectively, with the canteen occupying the ninth floor.

With the introduction on 5th November 1967 of the MRC, a fully-automated message switching system and the successor to the OTRU, at Cardinal House, the OTRU was closed down and the staff disbanded after four very successful and productive years.

However, as Cardinal House was sited above the Snow Hill railway tunnel in Cowcross Street, the MRC did not appreciate the heavy coal bearing trains passing beneath it on a regular basis and plans had to be temporarily abandoned with the consequent reopening of the OTRU whilst problems, including cracks in the building structure caused by excessive vibration, were being ironed out.

The decision was then taken not to extend the MRC but to reactivate the OTRU and keep it running at Electra House, whilst waiting for the TRC to come on stream. The TRC, promising a fully-mechanised system, would be considerably more advanced than the OTRU and the MRC. On 30th March 1969 the OTRU was back in action, fully staffed and working to its capacity of 35 circuits. And so it was that six years later, on 3rd July 1975, the OTRU finally came to the end of its life after more than 13 years in existence, when all its circuits were transferred to the new TRC system.

('Space Age' control console, MRC, late 1967)

(Business as usual in OTRU, June 1969)

By the early 1970s, despite the threat to jobs from the adoption of new technologies, the ITTS was catering for up to 20 new entrants per week, who spent one week in a lecture room at Cardinal House, followed by a week's 'on the job' training at Electra House. In addition hundreds more OTO2s would be undergoing further training in phonogram and teleprinter work as well as those facilitating their further training to become OTO1s, which would enable them to work on the overseas telegraph circuits. Advanced training for OTO1s in Service Dealing was also covered. At that time the Officer-in-Charge at Cardinal House was Charlie Paton, an Assistant Superintendent, with his deputy, mainly responsible for writing all the course material, being Dennis Wood. From an instructional staff of 90 OTO1s, three instructors would be allocated to each set of two groups of 10 trainees. By the mid 1970s the training school also offered a TRC course for senior OTO1s.

Cardinal House was to continue to house the company's training school until the late 1980s when it was run down and eventually closed and by mid-1991 the TRC was also closed down, to be replaced by a new relay unit at British Telecom's Coventry facility.

The building was eventually demolished in 2013 to make way for the new Farringdon Crossrail station. As is common practice in the vicinity of the City of London, an extensive archaeological survey was required before new development could commence, especially as it had been suspected that the building might stand on the site of the Roman West cemetery, with medieval plague burials also in the vicinity. The excavations did not reveal any Roman graves, but did unearth part of a 14th century 'Black Death' plague burial ground.

The site had also been close to the scene of a German V2 rocket attack on 8th March 1945, which hit the Smithfield meat market in the closing days of the Second World War, killing 110 people. Word had quickly spread in the surrounding area that a consignment of fresh rabbits had arrived and local housewives were anxious not to miss out on the possibility of some fresh meat. As V2s travelled faster than the speed of sound, there would have been no warning of its arrival. Sadly, many of the fatalities were women queuing for the meat.

Electra House on Strike

In 1969 big changes were afoot with the introduction in July of the *Post Office Act 1969* which allowed for the changeover of the General Post Office (GPO) as a government department, to the Post Office as a public corporation.

But prior to this, in January 1969 there began the first of two official strikes for better pay and a cut in the standard 44-hour week which was supported by the Union of Postal Workers (UPW) under its General Secretary, Tom Jackson (1925-2003), he of the luxurious handlebar moustache. According to Mr. Jackson the dispute was not about the amount of a proposed increase but that the increase was "dependent on conditions concerning productivity which had not been a condition for some 800,000 other civil servants being given the

(A strikebound Local Room, looking from west to east, January 1969)

same 5% rise". Led by Electra House Branch Secretary Ron Beak, most OTOs joined the strike, and Electra House and the area offices were brought to a virtual standstill. The Engineers in the POEU (Post Office Engineering Union) although not unsympathetic to their co-workers dispute, did not join the strike, as it was not their fight.

The then Post-Master General, under Harold Wilson, later to become the first Minister of Post and Telecommunications, was one John Stonehouse, later to find notoriety in November 1974 for faking his death, after leaving his clothes on a Florida beach and disappearing - only to be discovered and arrested on Christmas Eve that year, in Australia.

The police 'down-under' had initially thought that he might have been Lord Lucan, on the run after the murder of his children's nanny, and he was asked to remove his trousers to see if he had 'Lucky' Lucan's six-inch scar on the inside of his thigh! The scar failed to materialise but his true identity was soon established. He was eventually returned to the UK to face fraud charges,

(Zone 31, a deserted Press Section during the January 1969 strike)

receiving a seven-year prison sentence. The notoriety didn't end there however as it was revealed after his actual death in 1988 that he had been a spy for the Czech government in 1962 at the height of the Cold War! Perhaps a striker's placard back in 1969, enquiring 'What Kind of a House is Stonehouse?' hit the nail on the head. The strike was resolved but not very satisfactorily and in early 1971 a second strike of OTOs was to take place as part of a Post Office-wide dispute.

In the early 1960s it was agreed that a NASA (National Aeronautics and Space Administration) office would be set up at Electra House, manned by senior OTOs who would be trained by the Americans and who would work under a U.S. manager. They were to monitor data sent from spacecraft and satellites on behalf of NASA to ensure the quality of the signals and data transmitted to and from spacecraft. This was of prime importance as constant monitoring of the craft and astronauts could help prevent potential disasters.

The signals were put through an amplifying system and if too weak or garbled could be re-routed via a stronger signal. Signals could be switched to anywhere in the world including Australia as well as through ships at sea. The department worked with tracking stations in the U.S., Australia and Spain with additional voice links to these countries. The team, who were housed on the upper ground floor of Electra House in a room marked 'NASA, Strictly No Entry', by necessity led a secure and somewhat isolated existence whilst working on Gemini, Apollo and the Space Shuttle missions. During this time astronaut, and later Senator, John Glenn (1921-2016) visited Electra House, one of many famous visitors over the years.

Later, on 21st July 1969, that momentous achievement of putting a man on the moon took place. President John F. Kennedy had famously set the challenge in May 1961 in his address to Congress of "landing a man on the moon and returning him safely to earth by the end of the decade". Electra House was to play a not insignificant role in working with NASA to achieve that aim, sharing the incredible suspense of successive moon shots and in particular the dramas of July 1969 with Neil Armstrong, Buzz Aldrin and Michael Collins in Apollo 11 and later in April 1970, as the crippled Apollo 13 capsule limped safely back to earth on a 'wing and a prayer' with astronauts Jim Lovell, Jack Swigert and Fred Haise, Jr.

The NASA Room was to continue in operation until March 1984 when it was closed down after many happy years of collaboration between the two organisations.

By 1970 the overseas telegraph system, administered from Electra House, was in full flow, handling up to 50,000 telegrams a day, or about 1.5 million per month. Telegraph circuits were operated via High Frequency radio, co-axial cable, satellite and the old fashioned 'two-unit single-core cables'. The various methods of transmission and reception connected to the OTRU, MRC and Gentex switching systems, with 'a large residue' still working on a point-to-point basis. In addition, at that time, the International Telex Exchange (Intelex) at Fleet Building also handled 1.25 million messages.

A tally of staff numbers running Post Office Overseas Telegraphs in that year amounted to some 4,000 operators and supervisors, 250 counter staff and 350 postal staff. Superintendents at that time, responsible only to the Telegraph Manager, Mr. M. G. Bell, were J. S. Grant, A.G. Wilson, E. T. Mander and G. A. J. Hancock, with three Area Offices at that time run by E. C. Drewett, E. W. Stacey and E. E. (Eric) Smith and Intelex at Fleet Building by R. R. Baker. The MRC, based at Cardinal House, was headed by R. L. Farrant.

In January 1971 a second strike of Overseas Telegraph Officers took place as part of a nationwide Post Office walk out, following the breakdown of talks between the UPW and the Post Office Board, the managing body. It was known as the '47-day strike' and at its height an estimated 200,000 Post Office workers joined the strike. It followed the breakdown in negotiations over a pay rise. The UPW had asked for a 15% increase in pay, in line with recent increases agreed to in other major industries and not excessive in those days of high inflation, but were offered only 8%, linked to an increase in productivity. The Post Office were particularly intransigent in their dealings with the UPW and its General Secretary Tom Jackson, and no doubt were well aware that the union could only carry on the fight for a limited period until it ran out of funds and would be unable to borrow any more money from the banks.

The seven-week strike ended with no agreement between the parties, after the setting up of a committee of enquiry had been accepted by both sides, and with the UPW facing bankruptcy. The union had at that time amassed debts of £690,000 with a bank overdraft comprising some £340,000 of the total. There was no alternative but to order a return to work, despite angry protests from many strikers with some telegraphists at Electra House reported to be 'staging a sit-down strike against conditions being imposed since their return to work'. The subsequent Committee of Enquiry chaired by Henry Hardman, a former senior civil servant, resulted in a 9% pay rise, together with

(A view of Electra and Arundel Houses from the south east, June 1969)

improvements in the contentious age-related pay scale system which enabled OTOs to reach the maximum wage for their grade in a shorter time. The results of the enquiry were implemented in May of that year, back-dated to 1st January.

As with many strikes there was always the chance of 'blacklegs' continuing to work during the strike. Understandably there was considerable animosity towards such strike-breakers when the strike ended, not least because they too would benefit from the hard won improvements to pay and conditions, without having to experience the financial hardship experienced by the strikers. Such bad feeling could continue for many years with some people being 'sent to Coventry'. This was a phrase with later relevance when in the late 1980s some OTOs were invited to work from the BT facility based there.

Big changes to the company were discussed later in May of that year in a confidential report to the Post Office Board, who held the destiny of Overseas Telegraphs in their hands. At the time the 'International public telegram service' was losing £5 million pounds a year with the prospect of even bigger losses to come in future years, and something drastic needed to be done.

The long-term solution was of course further mechanisation, which in time meant fewer staff on the payroll. At the time 80,000 telegrams were handled on average every day, with 129 overseas circuits providing links to 73 countries.

They were sent and received in four different ways - at Electra House via OTRU, via point-to-point circuits and through the European Gentex system and also at Cardinal House, via the MRC. The report suggested replacing these four systems with a single computer-based 'stored program message switching' system, which could handle up to 100,000 messages a day. It was recognised that it would be more profitable for the company to use such a system rather than to expand the MRC. Three specialist companies, Plessey/ICL, Honeywell and Philips had been approached a few years earlier to research the problems involved and to tender for the work and the board was informed that Philips were the preferred candidate on grounds of system integrity, delivery time and cost.

Phase One of the system could be installed 'in the first half of 1973' at Cardinal House where interference with existing equipment would be minimal. The installation would mean the replacement of the MRC, OTRU and most of the point-to-point circuits but a decision by the board needed to be made by the end of May 1971 or the Philips design team as well as the ETE (External Telecommunications Executive) project group would have to be dispersed.

At that time there were some 3,400 operating staff working for the company, 2,300 being based at Electra House and Cardinal House. The remainder were spread between the four London area offices and the six main provincial ones. Under mechanisation, the report continued, "the staff requirement is expected to be halved". It was thought this could be achieved with natural 'wastage' through retirement as well as the considerable reduction in overtime. For some years it had been company policy to maintain a high level of overtime coverage instead of trying to recruit a full complement of staff. Whilst waiting for a new automated system to come on stream those high overtime levels would be maintained although the consequences of substantially reducing them in a short space of time would seriously affect many OTOs financially as it was not uncommon for an operator to increase their basic salary by 50% or even 100% by excessive overtime working.

Due to the substantial annual losses the report even looked at the possibility of closing down the service entirely – a prospect that surely would have had Sir John Pender and Sir Edward Wilshaw spinning in their graves! It stated that there was no specific international convention to prevent this but concluded that such action "would have a considerable adverse effect on the business interests of the country" as overall in the UK 75% of telegram traffic was for business purposes, rising to 90% in London. The report added that although the international telex service was gradually growing, many underdeveloped countries around the world still depended very much on the overseas telegram, and that no drastic overall reduction in telegram traffic was foreseen in the next decade. The then annual growth rate in traffic was 1% per year, with the number of telegrams at that time running at 20.3 million telegrams per year, with 6.2 million of them just transiting London.

Interestingly, the report noted that although the cost to the public of sending a telegram to a European destination had risen in March 1970, 'inter-continental' rates had not changed since 1957, despite rising costs. It suggested an increase in tariffs of 40–50% by the next year; with an expected 10% reduction in traffic as a consequence of the price rises. The Post Office Management Board, considered the report and the options it highlighted, and subsequently approved the placing of the order with Philips.

Later in 1971, following the October bombing of the Post Office Tower in Central London by the IRA, security at Electra House and other offices was stepped up and security passes for staff were introduced. The two exits from the rear of Electra House into Milford Lane and Tweezer's Alley were closed off leaving staff to use the side entrance off Arundel Street and the main entrance in Temple Place, which had been out of bounds to them for many years.

Around this time the Arundel House telegram acceptance counter office was fire bombed by two men who threw what appeared to be a petrol bomb through the entrance. They rapidly left the scene being hotly pursued by counter staff, but nobody was ever caught or convicted of the crime. It's possible that the IRA were involved as they were very active in London around that time, following the commencement of 'The Troubles' in Northern Ireland in August 1969, and exacerbated by the events of 'Bloody Sunday' in January 1972. Little damage was done but security was stepped up with a guard being placed at the entrance to Arundel House with the counter eventually being moved deeper into the building. There had been an earlier incident in 1944 when a hurricane lamp was thrown through a window of Arundel House. Nobody was caught and it was thought to be the action of a random drunk or mentally deranged person.

Chapter Five

The Last Days of the Telegram

In February 1973 the 'CP9' (Committee Paper 9) programme at Electra House divided the operating floors into units and Room Two became the Manual Switching Unit (MSU) for the next two years before the TRC arrived with its Visual Display Units (VDUs). The TRC was located at Cardinal House, the Philips DS714 system being installed on the first floor, and it went into service on 28th April 1975. The new system could safely handle up to 100,000 messages a day, using the then state-of-the-art computer technology, which also allowed for the electronic storage and retrieval of forwarded telegrams (up to 750,000) and in addition it facilitated the automatic receipt and delivery of messages into the Telex and Gentex systems. It also was designed to unpack delivery instructions for telegraphic addresses and deliver them by telex to UK subscribers, and it could store letter rate telegrams for automatic delivery by telex when appropriate.

The system lasted 16 years and was officially curtailed at the end of June 1991. It was obviously reluctant to end its role in 'handling' telegrams, as when the processor was switched off for the last time, the standby processor automatically took over, and it had to be turned off twice!

In 1981 the Telemessage Service was introduced. This involved a telegram of up to 50 words not including the address, 'sent by telephone or telex, and delivered in written form', generally by first class post the next day. It was a 'nail in the coffin' for the traditional telegram as it was to replace the standard telegram for inland delivery, traditionally delivered by messenger.

1st October that year also saw the introduction of the *British Telecommunications Act 1981* whereby responsibility for telecommunications was transferred from the Post Office, creating two separate corporations, Post Office Limited and British Telecommunications. British Telecommunications International (BTI) was set up and for the next ten years it oversaw the final days of the telegram with the decreasing roles of both Electra House and Cardinal House in a once-proud telegraph system. Three years later the *Telecommunications Act 1984* received Royal Assent and became law, as BT was privatised by Margaret Thatcher's Conservative government.

Despite the fact that the telegram played a declining role with BTI, the company prospered with a decade of technical expansion and development as

*Electra House, bracketed by Arundel House and 2, Temple Place
23rd August 1982*

technology embraced new systems of transferring information, whether for voice or data transmission. The telex services the company provided peaked in 1987 with some 200 countries connected to the network, but increasingly, whilst the cost of national and international calls fell continually, companies were employing fax machines to send hard copies of documents and necessary information, driving a further 'nail in the coffin' of the telegraph systems and signalling the demise of the use of telex.

The great increase in the 1980s of international telephone circuits was due primarily to the development of undersea fibre optic cables. These were first tested in 1980 when the *CS Iris* laid an experimental submarine cable in Loch Fyne, famous for its oysters and herrings, on the west coast of Scotland. The principle of transmitting telephone conversations via beams of light was nothing new, as way back in 1878 Alexander Graham Bell, that great Victorian pioneer of the early telephone, had first mooted it. A century later scientists had finally worked out the physics and practicalities of doing so by guiding high-speed pulses of light along hair-thin strands of glass.

Optical cables could carry far greater volumes of traffic, were free from interference and were cheaper than the old copper co-axial cables to operate, and were also made from a cheap material. They were also ideal for the digital communications of the foreseeable future with the Internet and the World Wide Web on the horizon, waiting to revolutionise all aspects of modern communication. The world's first operational undersea fibre optic cable was developed and laid by BTI in 1984 from Portsmouth in Hampshire to Ryde on the Isle of Wight, harking back to Marconi's early wireless experiments in the 1890s between the island and the British mainland. This was followed two years later by the first international fibre optic cable link, between the UK and Belgium carrying 11,500 circuits. This cable used just three repeaters to maintain the signal strength, rather than the dozens a traditional co-axial cable would have required. Within a short space of time fibre optic cables spread out around the world, retiring the old copper cable systems which had been the mainstay for the previous 130 years or more.

In November 1984 British Telecom changed its status from that of a Civil Service organisation to a truly commercial corporation with the flotation of 3 billion shares in the new company to the public. This was part of Margaret Thatcher's Conservative Party government's policy of selling many of the country's publicly-owned assets back to members of the public, albeit only those who could afford to buy the shares, a strategy which in another era or another country could have sparked a revolution. The sell-off proved a big financial success for the government, but if one 'sells off the family silver', as ex-Conservative Prime Minister Harold Macmillan referred to the process, it can only be done once. The change in status made little difference to the remaining Overseas Telegraph Operators, but by then the writing was on the wall for the poor telegram, as other faster and cheaper methods of communication had increasingly taken over its role in uniting society.

As the London area offices came to the end of their useful existence in the early 1980s, staff and the remaining services were brought back to Electra House. The Main Telemessage Office (MTO) was subsequently established on the sixth floor of the building until March 1991, when it was re-located to St. Botolph's in Houndsditch. The MTO used operator positions with VDUs (Visual Display Units) to route telemessages into the system. It also was home to a direct line to 'Buck House', or Buckingham Palace as it is better known, the Queen being a major sender of telegrams to her centenarian subjects.

By 1991 as telex, fax and direct telephone links became increasingly affordable and available to all, it was finally decided to end the OTO grade after decades of proud use. At that time a mere 30,000 words per day were sent by telegram, against two million at its peak, a peak that had lasted from the mid 1950s to the mid 1970s! Many operators opted for Early Voluntary Retirement (EVR) at age 50 or over – the end of an era and a sad day indeed! Some operators were given the chance of an enhanced pension especially if volunteering to retire early. The pension system was based on a maximum of 40% of a person's final salary when retiring at 60, but as the end of BT International arrived in March 1991, beneficial terms were on offer to some 'lucky' operators.

As early as the spring of 1987, talk was circulating about the future of Electra House as it was known that Cable and Wireless, as owners of the building, were offering the whole of the building to BT who did not particularly want it anymore. There was speculation that it might be converted to an hotel but it would then require a huge refit for that purpose. More likely it was thought to continue in use as an office block as there were clearly many more years of use in the structure.

On 18th February, 1989 Electra House closed its doors for the last time on its once-proud service, marking the end of an era. The writing had been on the wall for some time and by the summer of that year as a further insult in the eyes of many people, its name was changed to Globe House. From late 1990 for some three years, the building was used by the London Residual Body, which was charged with clearing up the affairs of the Greater London Council (GLC) which had administered the capital from 1965 until 1986, before being superseded by the Greater London Authority (GLA) headed by Ken Livingstone as the newly-elected Mayor of London. The building was subsequently acquired by 1991 by the Coal Board Pension Fund with plans to convert the building to conventional office space. The building was sold on again, this time to Hammerson Properties in December 1995 with prominent 'For Rent' signs appearing outside, but sadly by the autumn of 1996 demolition of the iconic building was in progress.

In keeping perhaps with its past overseas links, its doors were subsequently sold to a company in The Netherlands and its windows were shipped off to Italy and with demolition complete by 1997 the site was cleared for the building of it's successor, also to be named Globe House. Remarkably the building had been created to supersede one of the same name, and upon demolition was replaced by one of the same name, albeit it different to the original name.

Despite the fact that Electra House, Victoria Embankment had reached the end of its life as the world's premier telegraph office, it was not quite the last word on the site as a subsequent archaeological survey found evidence of previous occupation there from Roman times with a variety of pottery shards, flue tiles, etc., together with various other items from the Saxon and Medieval periods. As a farewell gift to posterity a cardboard box was found in the basement of the building during demolition work, containing three 'objects excavated during work on the site of Electra House, WC2, 1930-1931', a near complete Cheam ware bowl, a copper alloy spout from a jug and a complete iron spur with six-pointed rowel, or wheel, all dating from around the 14th Century.

In 1999 the new Globe House was completed and since then has been used as the London headquarters for the British American Tobacco company. The name harked all the way back to Sir John Pender's Globe Trust and Telegraph Company founded in 1873, and later in 1946 when the Globe Trust owned one-third of Cable and Wireless (Holdings) Ltd. The only visible signs of continuity from one building to the other are the two fine life-sized bronze statues of Mercury, the winged messenger, holding a caduceus, a short staff entwined by two serpents, which sit on their pedestals that have now flanked the main entrances to both buildings. The statues, with bodies modelled on the torso of Charles Assirati, a well-known body builder of the 1930s, were

(The end of an era, as EH is demolished, 1996)

designed by Sir Charles Thomas Wheeler, a one-time president of the Royal Academy.

And what of Cable and Wireless? Detailed histories of the company have been written, in particular '*Girdle Around the Earth*' and '*A Century of Service*', the latter being commissioned to celebrate the company's centenary in 1968. Other volumes of personal reminiscences of Cable and Wireless staff working around the world also make for interesting reading. Over the years they might have to face anything from hurricanes, earthquakes, famine, wars, revolutions and an assortment of tropical diseases, but you can be sure that keeping the circuits working was always of the highest priority.

The company was to continue to prosper through the telecommunications boom of the 1980s when its Mercury Communications subsidiary became the first rival to break the monopoly of British Telecom in the UK. It later invested in cable TV, eventually selling its interest to NTL (National Transcommunications Limited) in 2000. It remained a major player in the UK telecommunications market and in certain overseas territories, notably the Caribbean and South Atlantic areas, until after various acquisitions and

(Arundel and Globe Houses overlooking Temple Gardens)

sell-offs it de-merged in 2010 into Cable and Wireless Communications (CWC) and Cable and Wireless Worldwide (CWW). CWC was subsequently sold to Vodaphone, the multi-national telecommunications giant in July 2012 and CWW to Liberty Global, the world's leading cable company, in April 2016.

Ironically, the final Cable and Wireless shareholders' meeting was held at the offices of J. P. Morgan at 60 Victoria Embankment, just a stone's throw from the site of Electra House. At that fateful meeting a shareholder was heard to remark that, "Cable and Wireless was 164 years in the making, and only 45 minutes in the unmaking!"

As a postscript to the on-going life of Temple Place and Gardens, the controversial Garden Bridge over the River Thames was due to be built, linking the South Bank with Victoria Embankment on the north side of the river, with access to the bridge from above the existing Temple Underground station, just 50 metres from Arundel House. Fortunately or unfortunately, according to

(An artist's impression of the proposed bridge with green-roofed Globe House, Arundel House, centre left and the gleaming white HQS Wellington)

your viewpoint, the Mayor of London Sadiq Khan announced in April 2017 that as there was a 'funding gap of over £70m' he was not prepared to risk further public money on the project. His decision has effectively killed off the project unless new funds can be found from private investors.

The bridge, would have been 366 metres in length and had been designed by Thomas Heatherwick, based on an idea by actress Joanna Lumley, who with the strong support of the then Mayor of London, Boris Johnson, successfully promoted the project in its initial stages.

In May 2016 Khan, as the newly-elected Mayor of London, had given his cautious support to the project, but had insisted that the bridge would have to be open to all Londoners. The bridge would have only been open to pedestrians and would have provided a splendid platform to take in the London panorama from its mid-river viewpoint, without the noise and distraction of rush hour traffic.

Chapter Six

The People

The Telegraphists

Electra House, Victoria Embankment, was and is always affectionately known to OTOs as EH, in the same way as those other venerable institutions, the British Museum and Broadcasting House, could be referred to as the BM and BH respectively.

Any organisation spanning the best part of 60 years with 24-hour a day working and a staff roster of up to 3,500 people would inevitably include its share of characters, from the industrious to the workshy, from 14 year-olds starting work before and during the Second World War as the law then allowed, to retirees who came back to work after reaching the age of retirement, albeit generally at a lower salary grade. Stories and anecdotes of people and events taking place are legion, but perhaps best captured in another volume. Suffice to say that at Electra House 'all human life was there' and a school leaver joining the service had their education in the ways of the world completed in a very short space of time.

Due to the nature of the work of handling urgent and sensitive information it was required that all telegraphists, upon appointment, must sign the *Official Secrets Act*. Government messages in particular were, when possible, routed via cable to ensure security as radio messages could potentially be eavesdropped upon. Even in peacetime all governments went to considerable lengths to protect their own intelligence whilst gathering it from enemies or potential enemies. In addition, from a commercial point of view there was much sensitive information sent by telegram with the urgent transmission of stock and commodity prices, etc. especially in those pre-fax days when overseas telephone calls were an expensive luxury.

Each generation of telegraphists had to adapt periodically to changes in working practices, conditions and technology. None more so than those who served during the years of the two world wars, in particular the Second World War when both Electra Houses were potentially prime targets for enemy bombing and, as we've seen, both were severely damaged by German bombs.

Bearing in mind the nature and importance of sending and receiving telegrams, the emphasis was always on accuracy, although most operators combined accuracy with speed, as the training courses on the way to becoming an OTO1 always included substantial typing practice with regular speed tests. Operators taking the OTO1 course were also required in the early days to be able to send and receive Morse code and in later, post-war days, the requirement was to read 5-unit tape at a minimum of 16 words per minute, something which appeared difficult at first, before becoming second nature given time. Experienced senior operators in the 1930s and 1940s were reputed to be paid on a par with Members of Parliament, although there was a gradual decline in wage levels culminating in the industrial unrest in the 1960s and 1970s. One saying handed down to us is that if one couldn't get into Sandhurst (the military academy) then 'you could always try Cable and Wireless instead', and in fact in earlier years it was possible for one's family to pay for training as an operator, with those recruits receiving the designation OTO1a.

Day-to-day discipline was in the hands of supervisors who were generally promoted from OTO1 grade. Some gained reputations for following the rules to the letter whilst others were much softer in their approach, but most responded well to operators who worked hard to clear backlogs or keep a circuit running 'up to the wheel'. The general practice, especially towards the end of evening shifts was to allow a 'duty modification' or 'early off' in common parlance, which might allow an operator to leave up to an hour early provided the work was done or could be covered by another operator. This practice became an everyday occurrence, which most operators at Electra House and the Area Offices considered as their right. Over the years the 'dress code' became more relaxed as mandatory jackets and ties gave way to more comfortable sweaters and even jeans in due course, following the change in society's trends.

If operators transgressed by making a serious error in their work, or perhaps returned to duty seriously late from a break without a credible excuse, they could be issued with a written reprimand or a 'skin' as it was commonly known, the name being derived from the pink colour of the form being issued. They were also sometimes known as a 'forces sweetheart', the term derived from the Cockney rhyming slang 'Vera Lynn' for 'skin'. One supervisor no doubt remains in the memories of many ex-OTOs, a certain 'Skinner' Price, infamous for his strict adherence to the rules, which he 'defended' with relish, with no excuse for a transgression being accepted. Needless to say, he was uniformly disliked by operators under his supervision, as well as many of his fellow supervisors.

Annual Leave entitlement for OTOs increased with years of service and there was a system for taking uncertificated days off for minor ailments such as a migraine, often a euphemism for a 'hangover'. These days were agreed for the Civil Service in Great Britain by the Whitley Council, or Joint Industrial Council, a body comprising members of both labour and management, founded in 1919 and named for Mr. J. H. Whitley, the first chairman. 'Whitleys' as they were commonly known could be taken up to seven times in a twelve-month period, rising to ten days a year in the late 1960s. Absence for three or more days required the production of a doctor's certificate to avoid losing pay. Whilst OTOs regarded Whitleys as a 'right', management looked on them as a privilege and should one actually take the full entitlement in a year, the 'privilege' could be temporarily rescinded, an early example of 'Catch-22' perhaps.

Life at Electra House was not all work and no play and there were various distractions to fill breaks in shifts and after work hours. By the 1960s there were sports facilities on the seventh floor provided by ETESSA (the External Telecommunications Executive Sports and Social Association) where one could find full-sized snooker and table tennis tables. It was a wonder that some operators found the time to do any work at all. Many a game was curtailed by an urgent return to duty. For a few pence a week ETESSA offered the opportunity to play football, hockey, tennis, badminton and other sports including go-karting. There was even access to the rifle range situated in the basement of Somerset House, a few hundred yards to the west, along the Victoria Embankment. By 1984 ETESSA morphed into BTISSA (British Telecommunications International Sports and Social Association) and eventually into the perhaps unfortunately named BTIRA, the British Telecom International Recreation Association, before fading away.

No mention of the history of Electra House would be complete without mention of Mim's Café, sited next door to the entrance to Temple Underground station and opposite to a newspaper stand and fruit stall. It provided a perfect venue to watch the world (or was it just the girls?) go by, and especially during rush hours it seemed as if the whole world did go by as thousands of office workers poured out of the station entrance in the morning only to pour back in again at the end of the day, ready to repeat the process the following day. Electra House meanwhile would be working away ceaselessly connecting the world to itself day and night, day in day out, year after year without interruption.

('Mim's Café' 2017, how prices have risen over the years for a 'Full Engilsh!)

There was also a considerable amount of social interaction between the sexes at Electra House and many people formed relationships with fellow operators, often leading to marriage. To many people over the years, Cable and Wireless and its successors at Electra House - Post Office Overseas Telegraphs and British Telecom, offered not just employment but a virtually self-contained social life too. Whether one worked there for a few years or for their whole career, it provided an experience, never to be forgotten, and to many employees it was considered 'the best club in London'.

The Engineers

The work of the engineers at Electra House and other offices does not strictly come under the remit of this book, and in fact would no doubt merit a substantial volume of its own, but some mention must be made of whom they were and the valuable work they performed over the years.

Without the technical expertise of some brilliant engineers in designing, developing and maintaining the various machines and systems, the whole telegraph system could not have worked as well as it has over the past two centuries. The work of the early pioneers, from the likes of Cooke and Wheatstone, Morse and Marconi is well documented, but there were many more unsung heroes who made it all possible. In the latter years of the life of the telegram, in the post World War II period, from the 1940s to the 1990s, the rate of technological change increased considerably as electronic and computerised systems came on stream and as the world entered the era of the World Wide Web.

Over the years on a day-to-day level the engineer had to deal with a myriad of problems from simple machine failure to problems resulting from cable failure and interruptions in wireless communication due to atmospherics and other factors. In the periods of the two world wars they had all the additional problems caused around the world by those conflicts as cable stations fell into enemy hands and cables were cut, whilst on the home front both Electra Houses were bombed by the Luftwaffe with the resultant destruction.

In the immediate post war period of the 1940s and 1950s, as telegraphic traffic maintained its wartime levels and increased further, more engineers were recruited and trained. At its peak the engineering staff based at the Victoria Embankment building numbered around 200, which was not an excessive figure bearing in mind the 24-hour coverage required at Electra House and other buildings. In those days engineers trained primarily at Electra House either in the main repair workshops on the fifth floor or 'on the job' at one of the smaller stations positioned at the north west end of the building in the Local Room and the other operating rooms on the first, third and fourth floors. At that time they would also be sent to Government Buildings in Acton for general Morse training, including reading audio Morse, which they would be expected to read at 10 words per minute or more. Later, as 5-unit working became the standard, they would be required to learn to read that code as well.

A new recruit would start as a Trainee Technician (Apprentice) (TTA), rising in time to Technical Officer (T/O), and with seniority and service to

Assistant Executive Engineer. Basic training would take up to two years with a further three to become fully trained. All TTAs were allowed one day a week 'day release' for college attendance to be built into their work schedule in the early years, with all trainees studying for a City & Guilds qualification in telecommunications.

All necessary tools for the job were provided by the company, and these were mostly of Swedish manufacture, no doubt the best that money could buy at the time. Perhaps the most vital tool for a seasoned engineer would be the 'unbunger', a 'shim' tool used primarily to unblock punch blocks on teleprinters and perforators which were prone to getting 'bunged up' with paper dust and chads which resulted from perforating 5-unit tape in particular. Engineers were also supplied with the familiar full-length brown dustcoat.

Other areas within their remit included maintenance and on occasion operation of the emergency diesel generators in the basement of the building. These generators would not start running automatically if for any reason the mains power supply failed, and they had to be 'run up in synchronisation phase' before they could be used. Later, more modern emergency generators fitted to Cardinal House and other BT buildings such as Mondial House were automatically activated when required.

Other responsibilities included maintenance of the Muirhead facsimile machines housed on the fifth floor. These were in the care of specialist engineers. The Lamson vacuum tube system with its relevant compressors, was also maintained by the engineers, as well as the intricate rubber belt message conveying system, which linked the extensive operating rooms.

This system was fine when it worked smoothly, but once a jam occurred it could cause a pile-up of telegrams which might have to be retrieved, from eight feet above the ground, by using long-handled 'crocodile clips'. The rescued torn or creased message forms might also have burn marks on them.

Most engineers would become members of the POEU, which survived as a separate entity until 1985 when it amalgamated with the Postal and Telecommunications Group of the Civil and Public Services Association to form the National Communications Union. This was followed by a further merger, in 1995, with the Union of Communication Workers to form the Communication Workers' Union.

All in all, an engineer who remained with the company could expect a decent wage, good working conditions and respect for their expertise and a harmonious relationship with both the management and the general operating staff.

Chapter Seven

Telegrams and Telegraphic Equipment

The word 'telegram' deriving from the Greek *tele*, 'at a distance', and *gramma*, 'that which is written', is defined as 'A message sent by telegraph'. The term was first coined in 1852 in the *Albany Evening Journal*, published in the New York state capital, and has been with us ever since, despite the telegram itself falling out of use in recent years. In fact the last telegram sent by traditional means was purportedly that sent in India on Sunday 14th July 2013 to one Rahul Gandhi, although there are reports of far-flung regions of Russia still relying on the odd telegram and to this day there are companies in the UK and around the world, offering hand-delivered 'telegrams', targeting the market for wedding and birthday congratulations, albeit at somewhat inflated prices.

Apart from standard telegrams sent by cable or wireless from one country to another, the 'radio-telegram' introduced by Marconi in the early days of wireless, was vital for contact between ships at sea and shore stations. Over the years countless lives were saved through their use.

Another service available from the 1930s, was the photo-telegram, which generally involved a photograph or document sent by facsimile. This service came into its own during the Second World War when the newspapers of the world had an ever-increasing thirst for pictures of the conflict for their front pages and governments were hungry for images from war zones in particular.

Some well-known telegrams stand out from the countless millions sent over the years. Mark Twain famously cabled back home to America from London in 1897 upon hearing that his obituary was about to be published, "The reports of my death are greatly exaggerated". And a few years later in 1903 the first powered flight, by the Wright Brothers in South Carolina, merited the much more mundane "Successful four flights Thursday morning". Dr. Crippen and his lover, on the run and suspected of murdering his wife, were apprehended upon arrival by ship from Britain to Canada in 1910 with the aid of a telegram. After being spotted by the ship's captain, who sent a radio-telegram to Scotland Yard to alert the police, an enterprising police officer immediately took a faster sailing to overtake the fugitives and apprehend them when their ship reached its destination.

Unsurprisingly the wit of Oscar Wilde features amongst memorable telegrams when he cabled his British publisher from Paris to see how his latest book was doing. His message read "?", to which the reply came back "!", and in more

THE EASTERN TELEGRAPH COMPANY, LIMITED.

(Message Forms 5/1.)

LONDON.

Counter No.

Direct Cable Route with

AUSTRALIA, NEW ZEALAND, SOUTH AMERICA, EGYPT, INDIA, CHINA, JAPAN, STRAITS SETTLEMENTS, SPAIN, PORTUGAL, GREECE, TURKEY, and all parts of AFRICA, &c., &c.

HAND YOUR TELEGRAMS IN EARLY.

TELEPHONE NUMBER:	LONDON WALL 3240.		Official Instructions	TELEGRAPHIC ADDRESS:	"SIGNALLY, AVE, LONDON."

No.

Date.

Words.

Sent at

No. and Circuit

Code Time.

Charge.

£   s.   d.

" *Via Eastern* "

By

TO *Receiver's Name*

Address

THIS TELEGRAM WILL BE CHARGED AT FULL RATE UNLESS OTHERWISE INDICATED.

i request that the above Telegram may be forwarded subject to the conditions printed on back of this form by which i agree to be bound

Signature and Address of Sender

(Not to be telegraphed)

F.1.0.

To prevent mistakes attention is called to the importance of legible writing.

All important Telegrams should be repeated.— Quarter-rates extra charged for Repetition.

(1920s Eastern Telegraph message form)

recent times during the 1960 US presidential election campaign when John F. Kennedy, the president to be, joked that he had just received a telegram from his father Joseph, saying not to "buy one more vote than necessary" as he'd "be damned if he'd pay for a landslide".

Counter
Number..............

POST OFFICE TELEGRAPHS.

S.

IMPERIAL WIRELESS SERVICES.

FORM FOR

AUSTRALIA,
CANADA,

Via Empiradio

SOUTH AFRICA,
INDIA, etc.

(Also for **United States** and Countries reached through United States).

Date Stamp.	Prefix.	Service Instructions.	Words.	Sent.	For Postage Stamps.
		"Via Empiradio"		At................M.	*Any Stamp for which there is not room here should be affixed at the back of this form.*
	Code.		Charge. £ s. d.	To................ By................	*(A Receipt for the Charge on this Telegram can be obtained free of cost.)*

If this form is used for a Daily, Night, Week-end, or Post Letter Telegram, the indication DLT, NLT, WLT, or PLT, as the case may be, chargeable as one word, should form the first word of the address, otherwise the Telegram will be charged for at the full rate. (For information regarding these services, see back of form).

The Sender's Name and **Address**, or either of them, *if to be telegraphed*, must be written at the end of the text of the Telegram. Please write clearly.

TO

I request that the above Telegram may be forwarded *Via Empiradio* subject to the Conditions which are printed on the back hereof, and by which I agree to be bound.

Signature and Address of Sender..........................
(not to be telegraphed)

Notice.—This Telegram is accepted by the Postmaster-General for transmission subject to the Regulations as to Foreign Telegrams made pursuant to the Telegraph Acts, provided that the above *Request* is previously signed by the Sender.

(Post Office Telegraphs telegram, Via Empiradio, 1928)

Perhaps the most famous telegram of all was the final one sent by the *RMS Titanic* on 15th April 1912, which read "SOS SOS CQD CQD Titanic. We are sinking fast. Passengers are being put into boats. Titanic." (CQD originated from the use of CQ, from the French 'secu', derived from 'securite', which was to alert all stations of an important general message. The Marconi Company later added the letter 'D' to signify distress, especially at sea).

The telegram form has had a long and 'illustrious' history with many beautifully designed examples over the years, with different companies having their own individual style.

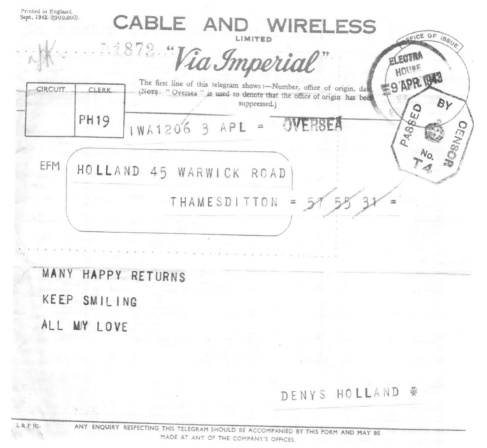

(Expeditionary Forces Message, 1940)

The primary telegram services available from British based companies, to and from Great Britain in the twentieth century in pre-Cable and Wireless days, were those offered by the Eastern Telegraph Company with their *'Via Eastern'* service, and from the Marconi Company where one could send a *Marconigram.*

By the late 1920s the Post Office were also offering overseas telegrams to Australia, Canada, South Africa, India, the U.S.A. and other destinations with their *'Empiradio'* service.

Once these companies were united as Cable and Wireless, one was encouraged to send messages *'Via Imperial'*, with later services, following nationalisation of the company being offered via Post Office Overseas Telegraphs, and eventually their succssors British Telecom.

In the post-war period, the classes of telegram available ranged from government telegrams on their distinctive red-edged forms to Urgent Rate, Ordinary, or Full Rate, to Urgent Press Rate, which were charged at half the price per word, to Letter Rate (LT, or ELT for European Letter Rate) and

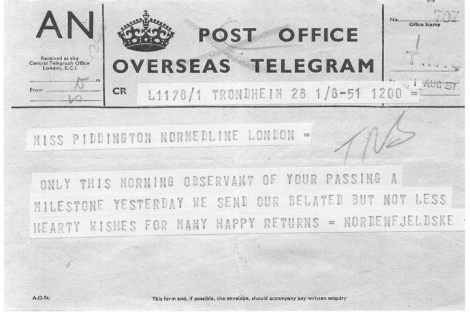

(A telegram from Norway, delivered to the City of London offices of a shipping company, from the Central Telegraph Office, August, 1951)

Ordinary Press Rate. In addition, Greetings Rate or Commonwealth Social telegrams described as 'Reduced Rate Plain Language Social Telegrams' (GLTs), were all charged at a quarter of the Urgent rate. Greetings telegrams were always popular over the years to be sent to couples getting married, with

(A one-time variation of the GLT telegram)

the Best Man required to read them out at the wedding reception to the assembled guests. Humorous texts with phrases such as "may your honeymoon salad always be lettuce alone" were to be found on occasion, but anything more suggestive or rude would have been rejected at the Office of Origin.

Urgent telegrams would have a red adhesive label attached to the top right-hand side of the message form to enable it to stand out whilst making its way along the internal belt system or if in a sheaf of mixed telegrams being routed or sorted.

It is worth noting that, in the latter part of the 20th century, Urgent rate telegrams were not accepted for destinations in the U.S.A., Canada and Mexico, as it was considered, especially by the North American cable companies, that all telegrams were priority messages.

There were also Mandats, or Money Order telegrams, popular with immigrants working abroad, for sending money 'back home' to family members, generally dotted around the Empire or Commonwealth. Common destinations in those days for Mandats included Sylhet in East Pakistan (now Bangladesh) and Poona (now Pune) in India. A Survey conducted in late 2015 for the World Bank estimated that 250 million people around the world were currently working abroad and sending money back home to relatives, with India being the largest recipient country. Most sizeable towns and cities around the world currently have a Western Union agent to handle international money transfers, with payments these days generally being transferred via the Internet.

Another telegraphic service available in days gone by was the LX Deuil, which offered a telegram, sometimes delivered on a black edged form, offering condolences or advising of a death, the French term 'deuil' translating as 'mourning'.

Government telegrams, using code words consisting of groups of five apparently random letters, were a common sight over the years. These messages would be prioritised and whenever possible, would be sent via a cable route, as wireless signals could potentially be eavesdropped upon. Typing such 'words' could be laborious for the operator as configurations of seemingly jumbled letters were not as easy on the eye as plain language, and typing them required strict concentration.

Another service, available to British forces posted overseas, especially after the Second World War, was that of Middle East telegrams sent to a MELF (Middle East Land Forces) address. In addition there were Forces Social (EFM) telegrams and Concession (CSN) telegrams. British troops were still stationed in Greece until 1952, Austria until 1955 and the Middle East until 1966, and these services played an important role in maintaining contact with friends and family back home. The bulk of such telegrams however were sent to BAOR (British Army of the Rhine), BAPO (British Army Post Office) and BFPO (British Forces Post Office) addresses.

Telegrams could be sent via other companies linked into the system, thus *Via Commercial* and *Via Western Union* were relayed to their respective American companies' offices, using a reciprocal quota system, *Via Northern* to the Great Northern company and *Via P.Q.* to the French Telegraph Cable Company which had a long history of linking Brest in Brittany on the French

CW 3/9.

TELEGRAM

MARK YOUR REPLY

POST OFFICE CABLE & WIRELESS SERVICES

OVERSEAS

GPO

OVERSEAS TELEGRAPHS

Send your reply
'VIA IMPERIAL'

TELEGRAM

(Envelopes for hand delivery showing the transition from 1950s to 1960s)

Atlantic coast with Saint-Pierre on the southern tip of Newfoundland by submarine cable. The majority of other telegrams handled by Electra House were of course routed *Via Imperial*.

From the 1950s telegrams were sent using the CCITT F31 format, designed to allow the automatic handling of telegraphic traffic. The CCITT (Comite Consultatif International Telephonique et Telegraphique) was the body set up in 1956, as part of the ITU, to standardise telegram formats for international telegrams as part of a wider series of standards covering the world of communications. The organisation issued recommendations which, although not mandatory, unless enshrined in the law of the relevant country using them, made perfect sense for all countries to comply with.

The standard layout for international telegrams (F31 format) evolved into a number line commencing ZCZC followed by any relevant serial numbers, then a pilot line with letters indicating the routing of the message. In earlier years these lines might have been in a more abbreviated form. The next line was the preamble line containing the Office of Origin, the word count and the date and time of filing. The following line showed the Service Indication if any, Urgent, LT, GLT, etc., to be followed by the address. The text then followed with the signature if any, to be followed by the Collation (COL) whereby any figures or unusual words would be repeated as a safeguard against error. The final touch after several line feeds would be the letters NNNN to signify the end of the message.

If the address or text included any words of more than 15 characters these would be charged as two words instead of one, and the word count in the preamble would reflect this with two figures separated by an oblique stroke, or forward slash in today's parlance.

Many commercial telegrams were sent to one word registered telegraphic addresses, which would be expanded at the destination office for delivery and accounting purposes, saving the sender the cost of sending a full postal address. They could be straightforward such as INTERFLORA GLASGOW, or perhaps abbreviated such as NATPROBAN LONDON (National Provincial Bank) or even discreetly reversing a name such as 'SELTAEB LONDON', being 'Beatles' spelt backwards. Others might have no obvious connection with the business they represented, BONIFACE LONDON being used by the Hong Kong and Shanghai bank.

Prior to his death in 1965, as Lord Warden of the Cinque Ports, Sir Winston Churchill's telegraphic address was 'WARDEN LONDON', whilst back in the 1940s MI5 used 'SNUFFBOX LONDON'. There was even a directory published, *Sell's Directory of Telegraphic Addresses*, in print for many years, which also offered companies' corresponding 'telephone numbers and classified trades'. At the start of the 1960s there were 48,000 telegraphic addresses in London alone. At that time 88% of telegrams for London delivery used registered telegraphic addresses, whilst the remaining 12% contained full postal addresses.

Other telegraphic addresses could contain two words plus the destination, thus in the 1930s, Electra House, Moorgate registered 'SIGNALLY, PHONE, LONDON' and the head office at Victoria Embankment used 'EMPIREGRAM ESTRAND LONDON' both addresses having a limited life span, albeit for different reasons.

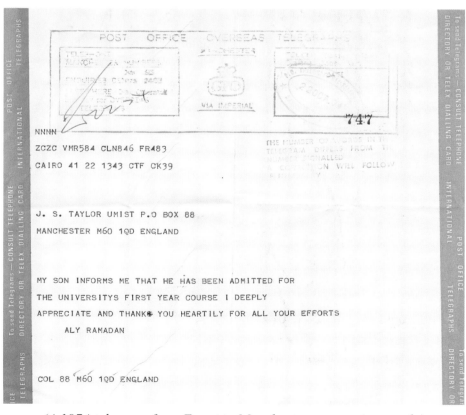

(A 1974 telegram from Egypt to Manchester, page printer style)

In later years, once the international telex system was established, one could also send a 'Telexogram', which was a telegram, charged at half the full rate, to be sent, at the request of the sender, directly from the telegraph office to a telex number.

And when all was said and done and a telegram had been delivered or forwarded to its overseas destination, messages were 'padded up' and sent to the LSA for accounting purposes and later for retention in the 'Dead Message Store', notably based in the 1960s at Radio House, Wilson Street, Marconi's erstwhile telegraph office and training centre. The Store was later moved to a Featherstone Street building, some half a mile to the north, near Old Street, before being eventually transferred to Cardinal House at Smithfield. Full-time staff (Service Dealers and Service Tracers) were employed to trace old telegrams and to respond to queries from overseas telegraph stations and commercial concerns relating to non-delivery and other assorted reasons. There was a statutory requirement to store 'dead messages' for six years before disposal.

Station Abbreviations and Service Codes

In days gone by Authorised Station Abbreviations were given to all destinations in the network. As Porthcurno is, to this day, referred to affectionately as PK, thus all other stations had their own designated two, three or even four letter code commencing alphabetically with AQ for Accra in Ghana and ending with ZU for Zurich. London was LN, New York, NYK and Tokyo, TO, all quite logical, but some were less straightforward with Ascension Island using AO and St. Helena, HL for example. Some names on the official list such as Talcahuano (a port city in Chile) sound strange to our modern ears whilst others perhaps have been subject to a name change in recent years – Bombay in India (now Mumbai) in particular, springs to mind.

'Q' codes for working on Morse transmissions were introduced by the British government in 1909 for use between ships and shore stations. Following the 1912 Radio Telegraph Convention a dozen three letter codes were standardised and quickly adopted internationally. They ran from QRA (what ship or coast station is that?) to QRN (are the atmospherics strong?), not forgetting QRM (are you being interfered with?), with QRE and QRI being omitted from the sequence. Their use has continued over more than a century since then, being adopted in more recent times by ham radio aficionados.

Five letter 'Z' service codes (pronounced 'Zed', rather than 'Zee', at least on the eastern side of the Atlantic) were also in use from a certain date. These could be found in the blue Service Codes book, a slim hardback originally published by Cable and Wireless, also available in languages other than English. The book contained hundreds of codes to choose from, depending on the required content of the service message. They started alphabetically with ABBAB, which the book would tell you meant 'Can you accept traffic for…', and culminated in ZYWAS, which stood for 'Unless otherwise instructed'. As you can imagine some were more popular than others and those such as AZWET - 'Cancel…' and POSRA - 'Herewith copy' were used on a daily basis. There was also a series of hundreds of three letter 'circuit' codes, also beginning with 'Z'. These ranged from ZAC - 'Advise (insert radio call sign) the frequency you are reading', to ZSU 'Your signal is unreadable' to ZXV, 'Your modulation is varying'. In addition a series of 'Y' codes were available for telex working.

In the days leading up to the First World War, the Marconi Company had also developed its own service codes, all with seven letters, with prefixes such as CID, DUX, JAP and SKO. Some were more strange or humorous to our eyes than others, thus DUXACNE stood for 'Cannot collect from sender', JAPDIZY for 'Is following for you?' and SKODAFT for 'Transmit at 70 words per minute'. Others such as JAPCLOT, JAPDAFT and JAPDRUG, although listed in the code book don't appear to have been used.

By the 1950s and 1960s Morse equipment was being gradually superseded by 5-unit equipment using the Murray Code. This code, which was developed in 1901 by Donald Murray (1865-1945), an inventor and electrical engineer, and one-time sheep farmer, who in later life studied philosophy in Switzerland. This code largely replaced use of the Baudot Code, which had been invented in 1870 by Jean Maurice Emile Baudot (1845-1903). Baudot's code was the first to use five units of equal length. The main manufacturer in the UK of teleprinters, transmitters and perforator keyboards using the 5-unit code was the Creed Company.

Creed Company Equipment

Frederick George Creed (1871-1957) was born in Canada and spent his early career as a telegrapher before what might be termed these days as RSI (Repetitive Strain Injury) no doubt caused by over use of a Morse key, forced him to consider other options to provide an income. The term telegrapher was in use from the early days but by the end of the 19th century telegraphist was more prevalent, in line with typists and other practitioners using that suffix. Whilst working as a telegraph operator for the South American Telegraph and Cable Company in Peru, Creed dreamt up the idea for a system enabling complete Morse signals to be punched onto a tape by using a typewriter-style keyboard. He relocated to Scotland where in 1895 he worked on developing a perforator keyboard, modified from a typewriter, using compressed air to punch holes in a paper tape and this became the forerunner of the teleprinter. He then went on to design a receiver perforator enabling punched tape to be converted to plain language.

The first orders for his machines came as early as 1902 when the British Post Office ordered 12 of them, and by 1909 he had set up his first factory, at Croydon in South London.

The company went from strength to strength, riding the wave of demand for teleprinters, not only from the Post Office but also from the commercial and press worlds. In 1928 Creed was taken over by the American International Telephone & Telegraph Company (ITT). The company continued its expansion

(The Creed 7b teleprinter)

(The Creed 7b teleprinter, with dust cover removed)

in line with the increase in telegraphic traffic and by the 1960s it had reached capacity at Telegraph House – its premises in Croydon. Unable to get planning permission to relocate in that area, the company moved south to Brighton in East Sussex, which was then encouraging new business to its Hollingbury Industrial Estate where Creed took over the old Underwood typewriter company premises. By 1967 the workforce numbered 1,600, rising to a peak of 2,000 by the early 1970s, making it the largest employer in Brighton. At the time its products were sold around the world but the biggest customer by far in those days was the British Post Office, which supplied telex machines to businesses, the armed forces, police and numerous other organisations, which relied on communication systems.

In 1975 the ITT Creed name was changed to STC (Standard Telephone and Cables) but by the 1980s demand for equipment fell dramatically as affordable computer systems came on the market, superseding some of Creed's products. In the mid 1980s the factory closed, the site being taken over by Asda supermarkets, which opened a new store there in November 1987.

The later Creed models ranged from the 3X tape printer, introduced in 1927 and in production until 1949, to the 7 series introduced in 1931 but still in use as the telegraphic workhorse of the post-war period, mostly with three-bank keyboards, for printing capital letters only, although some later models such as the 7F featured a four-bank keyboard. There were many variations with and without keyboards, some with reperforator units, some not. The standard speed of most teleprinters and transmitters was set at 50 bauds or 66⅔ words per minute.

Later teleprinters included the 47 model, introduced in 1947, the 54 produced from 1954, followed by the 75 model in 1958, with a four-bank keyboard. The T15 (or 444), also a four-bank model, appeared in 1968 to be eventually superseded by the model 23, also known as the ITT-Creed 2300. With the increasing demand for telex machines the four-bank keyboard became standard in the commercial world as office typists there were invariably taught to type on the larger 'standard' keyboard.

Another Creed product was the perforator keyboard, which allowed the operator to type messages on to perforated 5-unit tape. The tape roll fed from a hinged frame behind the plate where the messages being typed were attached. This independent keyboard was initially made with a black case and fitted with round keys comprising round frames covered with see-through Perspex exposing the relevant letter.

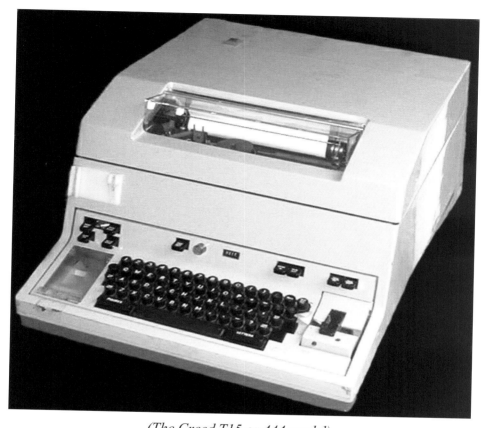

(The Creed T15 or 444 model)

Later models were issued with grey cases with green moulded plastic keys with letters stamped into the plastic. Perforator keyboards could enable several operators at a time to type batches of telegrams on to tape to be fed into a transmitter ensuring non-stop working of a circuit during busy periods. Operators soon learned to secure the punched tape by winding it around their thumb and little finger to make a 'drapers hank' to stop the tape from unravelling. A fast typist could hope to achieve speeds of 70 or 80 words per minute on such a keyboard, although the theoretical maximum speed was somewhat higher.

Creed also produced tape readers or transmitters, which read 5-unit tape and transmitted at 50 bauds, or 66⅔ words per minute.

(Creed perforator model 7P, introduced in the 1930s)

*(The Creed 5-unit 3-bank model 7P/N3 keyboard perforator,
in use from the 1950s)*

(The Creed 5-unit tape reader or transmitter)

Other major companies producing telegraphic equipment over the years were the Kleinschmidt Company, the Teletype Corporation and Lorenz in the U.S.A, Siemens in Germany, Olivetti in Italy and Sagem in France.

Appendix I

The Central Telegraph Office

The Central Telegraph Office was an imposing Victorian structure built in 1869 of granite and Portland stone and originally four storeys high. Its site bordered St. Martin's Le Grand, Newgate Street and Bath Street, so named for a 17th century Turkish bath.

The site was originally occupied by the church and sanctuary of St. Martin's Le Grand, which pre-dated the Norman Conquest and had a long and chequered history with connections to amongst others, Wat Tyler. Tyler, the leader of the Peasant's Revolt in 1381 dragged one Roger Lyatt from the high altar of the church and decapitated him in nearby Cheapside, incurring the wrath of the law for violating sanctuary and perhaps worse at the time, incurring the wrath of God.

It also saw Miles Forrest, one of the alleged murderers of the Princes in the Tower, "rot away piecemeal" according to Sir Thomas More, unable to leave the sanctuary of the church and under the rules of sanctuary unable to be fed. The right of sanctuary continued in practice until 1697. The princes had disappeared, presumably murdered in 1483. The main suspect for the murders was Richard III, whose grip on the throne would always be threatened by the existence of the princes, but no firm evidence has ever emerged of his guilt and it has to remain one of history's great unsolved crimes. St. Martin's church was demolished in 1548 during Henry VIII's Reformation, when countless monasteries, churches and other religious establishments were ransacked and destroyed at the behest of the king.

As the popularity of sending telegrams around the country increased, a fifth floor was added to the CTO building in 1884. In its Victorian heyday it was the largest telegraph office in the world and boasted links with all the major towns in the UK. At the peak of its popularity, immediately following the Second World War it handled 64.9 million telegrams a year, against 45,000 in 1880.

A vital part of the CTO's function was to send urgent messages via an elaborate system of up to 52 vacuum tubes connecting it to the War Office, the Bank of England, the House of Commons and various post offices as well as the Reuters News Agency and the Press Association and assorted newspaper

(The 'Centre' gallery at the CTO, pictured in 1935)

offices. The CTO was also rumoured to be connected in this fashion to the Prime Minister's residence at 10, Downing Street. The tubes had mostly been installed early in the 20th century and served a vital purpose for some 50 years, using a 'suck and blow' system powered by electric motors powering compressors. The tubes were cased in lead and laid beneath the streets of London and mostly remain there to this day, it not having been financially viable to remove them. The extensive brass tubing for the vacuum system situated in the building was subsequently removed from the vacant premises by Temple Mills Limited for scrap in 1963.

The CTO, situated a few hundred yards from St. Paul's Cathedral, had the dubious distinction of being damaged by enemy action during both world wars. It was initially struck on the south east corner of the fourth floor by a bomb dropped in an air raid in 1917 by a Zeppelin airship during the First World War. This was one of 103 German raids between 1915 and 1918, which unleashed 8,578 bombs, killing 1,414 people and wounding 3,416 others.

(The CTO illuminated and bedecked with flags for King George V's Silver Jubilee in May 1935, with St Paul's Cathedral beyond it)

The building was hit again, causing much more extensive damage, on 29th December 1940 during the Blitz of the Second World War, when it was set alight by burning debris from an adjacent building. It was not alone on that fateful night with 1,500 fires reported, as the City of London faced the greatest conflagration since the Great Fire of London, 274 years earlier in 1666. Dramatic photographs taken the next morning from the top of St. Paul's Cathedral by a policeman showed mountains of debris where whole streets had been the day before, but miraculously St. Paul's had not only survived the night but was virtually unscathed.

Interestingly, the present St. Paul's, despite its dominating presence, is only around two-thirds of the size of the original building, being 365 feet high, against 520 feet, and 513 feet long, against 690 feet. In medieval times with most buildings in the City of London being wooden and generally not more than a few storeys high, the Old St. Paul's, built on Ludgate Hill, had absolutely dwarfed any City building other than another church.

(The CTO in 1942, still some way off from re-opening)

The interior of the CTO was completely gutted that night, but rebuilt as a matter of priority and it re-opened in June 1943 albeit without its two top storeys. Luckily at that time much of its work had been temporarily transferred to the outskirts of London, and there were no fatalities.

Adding to the GPO presence in the street, and exactly opposite the CTO, in St. Martin's Le Grand, between numbers 18 and 40, standing side by side, were Armour House and Union House, both owned by the Post Office and built on the site of the grand Victorian General Post Office headquarters building (1829–1912). Armour House was severely damaged in 1940 by a parachute mine whilst Union House, which housed the Postal and Telegraph Censorship Department, survived the Blitz virtually unscathed.

After the war, between 1945 and 1947, the CTO building was further restored but as the growth in telephone and direct-dial telex use began to affect the market for inland telegrams, the building presided over a slow decline, and was never likely to regain its pre-war eminence. From 1958 when the Post Office's Continental telegram radio circuits were transferred to Electra House, its staff began re-locating, with the Continental teleprinter circuits following

(Business as usual in the 'North' gallery, 1949)

in 1960, and it finally closed its doors in October 1962. Its operators had gradually been transferred to other locations, some to the new Fleet Building and others to Electra House where many of the Inland telegraphists retrained as OTOs.

Depending on their grades, operators that re-located to Electra House from the CTO were initially restricted to certain duties. Those classed as OTO2s were only allowed to work in the Phone Room and on TAS receiving, gumming messages on to telegram forms. Those senior CTO operators given OTO1 status, primarily worked with Service messages, but in due course all those who transferred were given the necessary training to fit in with the rest of the Electra House operating staff. During the initial period after the transfer the new 'recruits' were referred to as part of the 'Enclave', an enclave in the wider world being 'a portion of territory surrounded by a larger territory whose inhabitants are culturally or ethnically distinct'.

('CTO corner', St. Martin's Le Grand and Angel Street, October 1962)

In the latter days of its use, there had been difficulty with staffing the CTO, as many OTOs based at Electra House were reluctant to transfer there due to the poor conditions prevalent in the building. Working with equipment contained in a confined space with poor ventilation could prove extremely oppressive, with cases of operators even fainting in the excessive heat. Thus many people were more than happy to relocate to better-ventilated premises when the building closed down. At one time, due to the lack of volunteers, the management at Electra House introduced a ballot system whereby the majority of people in the ballot were sent to the CTO. It was not a very fair one, as in fact one had to 'survive' three ballots before the threat of transfer was withdrawn. Some OTOs even became 'Commuters', spending the first half of their shift at the CTO then making their way to Electra House a mile away to complete the second half.

The building was then to lie empty apart from partial use for storage by the adjacent Post Office Headquarters building, until it was declared unsafe and it was eventually demolished in 1967. The site was to remain derelict until 1979, providing the archaeology department at the nearby Museum of London ample opportunity to excavate it, revealing a Roman burial ground and mosaics. In that year planning permission was granted for a new building on the site, the BT Centre, also clad in Portland stone and sitting on a granite plinth, it became the present headquarters of BT, being completed in 1984.

Appendix II

Fleet Building

Work on Fleet Building began in May 1959 and it was operational by December 1960. The opening ceremony was duly performed by Sir Frederick Alfred Hoare, the then Lord Mayor of London, on 11th May 1961. A year later he was to become the first Baron Hoare of Fleet Street.

The 13-storey building, a prominent modern concrete structure reflecting Harold Wilson's "white heat of technology", was the successor to the old Central Telegraph Office at St. Martin's Le Grand, and was the largest new Post Office building built since the Second World War. It occupied much of a large site between Shoe Lane and Farringdon Street, at one time sharing the block with the *Evening Standard* newspaper and the *Agence France Presse*, news agency, with Stonecutter Street and Plumtree Court completing a rough rectangle. Sitting on land once reclaimed from the banks of the Fleet River, it was just a few hundred yards from Ludgate Circus and Fleet Street, the then home to all the major daily newspapers. Fleet Building looked out to the east over Farringdon Street, with the facade of the building, at street level, decorated by a series of murals, comprised of ceramic tiles, designed by Dorothy Annan. They depicted futuristic designs "reflecting the atmosphere of optimism and excitement about new technology and communications in the 1950s and 1960s" according to English Heritage who obtained a Grade II listing for them in 2011 as plans for redevelopment of the site began to take shape.

The main access, on the western side of the building, was at 40, Shoe Lane. It boasted a canopied entrance displaying the inscription Fleet Building in an italic script, whilst the staff entrance was on the opposite side of the building.

Farringdon Street, named after a medieval City goldsmith, was constructed over the subterranean Fleet River or Fleet Ditch as it became known, flowing on its way to join the River Thames by Blackfriars Bridge. One may think the name Fleet derives from a term for a fast flowing river, which at times no doubt it was, but in fact it comes from the Anglo-Saxon Fleot – a tidal inlet. Several lanes that once led to the river still bear evidence of waterside activity with names such as Sea Coal Lane and Turnagain Lane, which is a cul-de-sac, or blind alley leading up away from Farringdon Street in the direction of Snow Hill. Interestingly in the past it was a cul-de-sac in the other direction, with access down from Snow Hill, but blocked when it met the Fleet River.

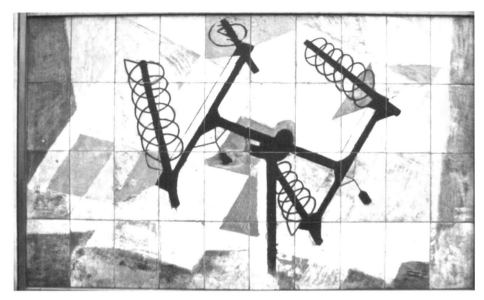

(One of Dorothy Annan's murals, now re-sited at the Barbican Centre)

Several hundred years ago the whole area was a network of hovels and slums with attendant high levels of disease, prostitution and crime, with the Fleet River little more than an open sewer. The river was arched over in 1736 and was never to see light of day again. The reclaimed space, approximately where Farringdon Road now stands, provided the site for the great Fleet Market which survived until 1829 when it became too dilapidated and was cleared away.

Fleet Building housed 'state of the art' equipment for operating the International Telex Exchange, or London Switchboard as it was known, with manual cordless switchboards manned by Overseas Telegraph Operators (from 1963) as well as the Inland Telegram Exchange (both on the third floor), plus International and Inland test rooms. It also housed two Telephone Managers' offices and the Fleet Mux (ARQ terminal) ('a radio telephony protocol to reliably forward telex messages over partially reliable radio') and an MCVF (multi-channel voice frequency) terminal. The International Telex Exchange had capacity for 12,000 subscribers and was to be the only existing international telex exchange until 1970. The OTO2s generally monitored subscribers connecting to European destinations, whilst OTO1s mostly

*(Fleet Building, and Shoe Lane, from the south west,
curiously devoid of traffic, September 1966)*

handled inter-continental connections. The administrative staff were housed on the twelfth floor whilst at the other end of the building there was an underground car park.

The Inland Telegram section handled up to 25,000 telegrams a day and was staffed at its height by over 600 operators, supported by the Delivery Office, for the EC3 and EC4 areas, from where the Messengers operated.

The building also offered a large first floor dining room, a lounge, a games room, a first-aid room, a large hall for 'social gatherings' and at one time it was also home to the 'Museum of Telecommunications Equipment and Techniques'. This was later transferred, in 1982, to the BT Museum at Baynard House, Blackfriars, where it was open to the public until 1st August 1997 when it was no longer deemed financially viable to continue with the museum. In 2001, it was replaced by the Connected Earth Initiative whereby its exhibits were distributed around other national museum collections, in conjunction with a detailed virtual museum on its website (www.connected-earth.com).

(New cordless switchboards at 'Fleet' in August 1962, ready for the off)

Fleet Building also had the distinction of having the first International Subscriber Dialling (ISD) call made from its premises, by the then Lord Mayor of London, Sir Ralph Perring, on March 8th 1963. Dialling 13 digits, he called M. Jacques Marette, the French Minister of Posts, Telegraphs and Telephones, in Paris. Prior to this, all overseas telephone calls had to be put through manually by an operator.

Being situated between Fleet Street and the Smithfield meat market areas, with their night and day activity, there was always a good choice of local pubs to frequent including The Hoop and Grapes, The White Swan, and not forgetting The Old and New King Lud pubs and the 24-hour Dunkin' Donuts 'restaurant', a strange American import at the time. The Press Club bar in Shoe Lane was also a popular haunt at one time.

Fleet Building also had the honour of hosting the semi-final of the 1964 GPO-Miss Interflora Personality Girl competition. This annual competition was initiated in 1959 and was open to all GPO telephonists, telegraphists and assistant supervisors in the UK. From the twelve semi-finalists, three, including Electra House OTO Hilda Ferguson, were chosen to compete in the grand final that was screened live on BBC1 on 14th July of that year. The final was transmitted from a BBC television studio and was hosted by the marvellous Kenneth Horne of the hit BBC Radio comedy show '*Round the Horne*'. Hilda went on to win the competition, being awarded a £100 first prize, and was pictured next day on the front page of the *Daily Sketch* with the then Post-Master General, Reginald Bevins, who had presented her prize. Along with the two runners-up she was flown off to the then exotic holiday destination of Alassio in Italy for a two-week all expenses paid holiday. A short film survives showing the three finalists at work and at play, prior to the final, with Hilda shown entering Electra House via the main entrance and at work in the building.

As winner of the competition, Hilda was also given a splendid lead crystal vase which for some years was put on public display. Upon her retirement in the early 1990s, it was unearthed from the back of a cupboard to be presented back to her. As it had no doubt accumulated many years of grime by then, it was taken off to a washroom to be cleaned before the handover, but as luck would have it, it was dropped onto the floor and broken into many pieces. One can imagine the horror of the perpetrator of the act and after a shamefaced confession, a new crystal vase was hurriedly purchased for poor Hilda.

The capacity of the International Telex Exchange expanded from an initial 60 operating positions with a queuing system for up to 25 calls, up to more than double that figure, but with an aging system always under stress its days were numbered. In the late 1980s after many changes of plan, the Exchange was transferred to Keybridge House with an increased capacity of up to 150 positions, although by then the writing was on the wall for the system, with more and more telex subscribers able to dial directly overseas themselves, plus more affordable overseas telephone calls being available.

15-storey Keybridge House was built in 1975 at Vauxhall, south of the Thames, with architecture since described as 'brutalist' and as an 'eyesore' and it had been frequently cited as the 'ugliest building in London'. Now it is no more, having been demolished in 2016 to make way for a new housing development that promises to be the tallest residential building in London.

Fleet Building continued in various uses under BT through the 1990s but by 2006 it was lying derelict and boarded-up. Shortly afterwards the site was sold to Goldman Sachs, the American multinational investment bank, for development as their European headquarters. Since the purchase of the site and commencement of the new building, Britain has opted to leave the EU, which has seriously affected Goldman Sachs plans as some of their staff destined to be based at the building are being relocated to an EU country. Demolition work on the building began in early 2014 and due to the extensive size of the building it was not completed until the end of that year. The new building, costing £350m and providing 1.1 million square foot of office space, is being constructed by Brookfield Multiplex and is due for completion in 2019.

Appendix III

London Area Offices

Broadway

(1A, Broadway, SW1)

Broadway area office, with a SW1 postcode (later extended to SW1H 0AU), was situated at 1A Broadway in Westminster just a stone's throw from Westminster Abbey and the Houses of Parliament and it served the SW1 postal code area. The telephone number to file messages from the local area was SULlivan 7255.

Opening in early 1964, and closing in the early 1980s, the office was modern, well-lit, with good natural light and fitted out with brand new equipment. The operating room was on the fifth floor, with the staff canteen one floor above.

Being situated near the seat of government with various foreign embassies within its range, it handled much sensitive traffic. The building also housed a telephone exchange, and survives to this day, still owned and run by the Post Office and used primarily to house the exchange and for storage. There is also a Post Office counter office sitting at street level, alongside the main building.

Being in such an historic area of London, it should be no surprise that the site of the Broadway office has an interesting and chequered history. The street was originally the site of a hay market and in the early 18th century one infamous local occupant was reputed to be highwayman Dick Turpin, no doubt keeping an eye on the road heading west from Westminster village. In 1642 the Broadway Chapel had been built there, and this was replaced by the imposing Gothic Christ Church in 1847. This church was in turn destroyed by the Luftwaffe in a hail of incendiary bombs on 17th April 1941 in one of the worst nights of the Blitz, and eventually in 1959 the present building was erected.

Broadway, a relatively short street, and not particularly broad, at least by modern standards, is famous in recent times for the classic 55 Broadway building, just 100 yards from 1A, and for many years the headquarters of London Transport. It sits opposite a non-descript building at number 54, which once displayed a plaque proclaiming it to be the home of the Minimax Fire Extinguisher Company. This was later revealed to have been a 'front' for the headquarters of the Secret Intelligence Service, later to be known as MI6, which used the building from 1926 to 1964. And half way between those buildings and 1A, sits *The Feathers* pub, a late Victorian structure with its high ceilings, its real ale and its imposing façade – the refuge of many a telegraphist in its day. One could perhaps imagine an OTO, a London Transport worker and a proto-James Bond all rubbing shoulders at the bar after a hard day at the office.

Across the road from the Broadway office building was New Scotland Yard, the headquarters of the Metropolitan Police Force. The building had been their base from 1967 until 2016 when it was sold for £370m to an investor from Abu Dhabi who is in the process of demolishing the building to make way for a 268 home development. Upon the sale the Metropolitan Police moved to the Curtis Green Building on the Victoria Embankment which was previously known as Whitehall police station, and it has now been renamed New Scotland Yard.

(Broadway office, February 1964)

Livonia Street

The Livonia Street office was set in the heart of Soho in London's West End at 1-7 Livonia Street, W1 (later W1V 4NB), and was tucked away just off Berwick Street. This street is home to a thriving street market and an eclectic mix of businesses ranging from specialist restaurants and cafes to the bars and sex shops the area was, and is still, famous for. Opening on 14th February 1964 and closing in August 1980 the Livonia Street office covered the W1 postal district for that 16-year span. The initial manager of the office was Roy Baker, a well-respected man who ran the office for several years. Several other managers followed him including Mr. S. A. Verrier, appointed in June 1973.

Livonia Street had previously been named Bentinck Street, being renamed in 1894. The name Livonia originated from a Grand Duchy with Polish associations and the naming of the street is thought to allude to nearby Poland Street. Soho had originally been under church ownership before being surrendered in 1536 to Henry VIII, who used the area as a hunting park for his Whitehall Palace.

(Livonia St. office in October 1963, prior to its February 1964 opening)

The office layout comprised a long narrow operating room with good natural light, on the first floor of the building, which it shared with the engineering staff and the manager's office. The canteen and rest room were situated on the second floor. The basement housed lockers and a boiler room. There was also an Adrema position, later increased to two as demand rose amongst account customers.

As with the other three area offices Livonia Street was opened to cope with the demands of the area, which were primarily based on the needs of central London hotels. In addition to the private customers in the area there were various import/export businesses, travel agents, theatres and even the Beatles Apple Corps Ltd, at 3 Savile Row, in the heart of the high class tailoring district, all needing to send and receive overseas telegrams on a regular basis. Locally-based customers could 'phone in their telegrams by calling REGent 2891.

In the early days as there were not enough volunteers to transfer there from Electra House, some operators, especially OTO2s, were drafted in with very little say in the matter. But they soon found life there to be acceptable and they benefited from the advantages of working in a smaller office. Soho was certainly a very interesting area to work in with its Berwick Street market, cinemas, restaurants and its proximity to the Oxford Street shops, not forgetting the seedier side of things on offer in the area.

Under the leadership of Roy Baker, the office developed a good social scene with children's parties, Saturday night dances in the canteen and even cheese and wine events with staff bringing in their art works to share with colleagues. One event, which might have drastically curtailed the use of the office, was a basement fire in the mid 1960s, when a burst oil fuel line resulted in the oil igniting. Luckily, the fire brigade was called promptly and the building evacuated whilst the firemen made short work of the blaze.

Although spoilt for choice for socialising after hours, many staff members favoured The Blue Posts, in Berwick Street, one of three pubs of that name in Soho. For night staff wishing to imbibe, throughout the lifetime of the office, licensing laws restricted the sale of alcohol to 11pm on weekdays and Saturdays and 10.30pm on Sundays. One could always become a member of a private club in the area though, which would enable one to drink after hours, but this could prove beyond the means of the average OTO.

Falcon House

Falcon House opened in October 1965 in EC1 (later EC1A 4ET), primarily to cover the EC1 and EC2 postal districts of the City of London's square mile. With an initial complement of 70 OTO1s and 76 OTO2s handling thousands of telegrams a day, it was a larger office than those at Broadway or Livonia Street. Taking its name from the adjacent, but long gone 17th century *Castle and Falcon Inn* in Aldersgate Street, and from what had been the adjacent Falcon Street, Falcon Avenue and Falcon Square, all three thoroughfares being swept away by the bombing of the Second World War, the office mirrored many of the systems then in use at Electra House, catering for the City's needs by day and night.

The first Manager was Ted Drewry, a kindly man, well-liked by the staff. Upon his retirement a year later, Eric Smith a much more authoritarian figure took over. It was generally a well-run, happy office, with a thriving football team and good social interaction between all grades, facilitated somewhat by the office's proximity to two nearby pubs, *The Lord Raglan* in St. Martin's Le Grand, and *The White Horse* in Little Britain.

Whilst the rear of the building overlooked Noble Street, the front entrance faced onto St Martin's Le Grand, across the street from Postman's Park and close to the site of the old *Bull and Mouth* coaching inn, which was demolished in 1888. The name of the inn, with its impressive wooden galleried structure built around a large courtyard, derives from *Boulogne Mouth*, which refers to the harbour and town besieged by Henry VIII in the 16th century. Postman's Park, named for its popularity with generations of postal workers was the brainchild of G. F. Watts, a Victorian painter and philanthropist. He suggested the park should be created to celebrate Queen Victoria's Diamond Jubilee in 1897, as a tribute to the 'heroic men and women' who had given their lives attempting to save others, generally rescuing them from fire, drowning and railway accidents. The park contains a gallery with ceramic plaques, each of which commemorates an individual act of bravery.

The Falcon House operating room was on the first floor of the building, and it was capable of accommodating perhaps 60 OTOs at any given time. With windows running along both of the longer sides of the large rectangular room, there was maximum use of natural light during daylight hours. In addition there were various offices on the ground floor and a canteen housed in the basement.

(OTO1 positions, Falcon House 1965)

Interestingly, the building experienced some supernatural episodes, if accounts can be believed - the first in the 1960s apparently featuring a poltergeist, when distressed canteen staff were reportedly terrified by plates 'sailing across the kitchen and smashing against the white tiled walls'. Later, in the 1970s there were reports by staff members, including a night supervisor, who witnessed strange apparitions in the staff restroom and unoccupied offices, resulting in the refusal of staff members to go there unaccompanied, especially at night. One may take such reports with a pinch of salt, but Falcon House was reputedly built on the site of an old cemetery, which would only serve to support the reports in some eyes.

Falcon House was to close as a telegraph office in the early 1980s and between 1997 and 1999 following the demolition of the building and the

(Adrema positions at Falcon House, staffed by OTO2s, 1965)

commencement of a replacement building, an archaeological survey uncovered *'Roman features'* - not surprising perhaps as Falcon House stood immediately outside the wall of the old Roman fort, at its south western end. The fort, built in around 120 A.D. and running along what is now Noble Street, was incorporated into the later wall, built around 200 A.D., that surrounded the Roman city, with substantial traces of the structures still in existence next to the site of Falcon House to this day.

St. Botolph's House

Situated at 138-139 Houndsditch, EC3 (later EC3A 7ND), close to Aldgate in the City of London, 'St. Bots' was the last of the four London area offices to open. It was a typical modern 1960s building with clean lines and large areas of glass incorporated into the structure giving good natural light.

Opening in 1967, with Eric Smith, transferred from Falcon House, as one of the first managers of the office, it provided a similar service to the other three area offices at Broadway, Livonia Street and Falcon House, but mostly serving customers in EC3.

(St. Botolph's House, main entrance, 1967)

Houndsditch, sitting adjacent to and running parallel with the old Roman city wall, acquired its name from the ancient practice of disposing of waste, and in particular deceased dogs in a one-time defensive ditch there. Although the name Houndsditch was first recorded in 1275, the practice may well be of an earlier date as some canine skeletons from the Roman period were excavated there in 1989. Houndsditch runs one-way between two churches, St. Botolph's Without Bishopsgate and St. Botolph's Without Aldgate, and there were also two other churches dedicated to the 7th century saint, the patron saint of wayfarers, at Aldersgate and Billingsgate, although this last one was lost in the Great Fire of London in 1666. In more recent times the street was famous for the Houndsditch Warehouse, described as 'The Selfridges of the Jewish Quarter', a large department store mostly selling clothes. The store opened in the early 1920s and was to close in 1986.

The office was open for some 15 years and proved popular with many staff members. Back in those early days favoured 'watering holes' in the vicinity were *The Bell Tavern,* and *The Clanger,* now replaced by a 'stylish City bar' the *All Bar One.*

In addition to its role as a telegraph area office, St. Botolph's House was home to various other facilities including a Post Office at street level and by 1971 there were plans to install a telex exchange in the building, as the planned

(St. Botolph's House, east wing, 1967)

home for the exchange at Keybridge House would not be ready in time. In addition, by the late 1980s the Telex/Fax Bureau was based at St. Botolph's. St Botolph's was to close down by 1991 by which time its useful days were over.

The site is now occupied by the St. Botolph Building, completed in 2010, and currently occupied by a large commercial and retail scheme including the Jardine Lloyd Thompson Group, one of the world's largest insurance, reinsurance, brokerage and 'employee benefit solutions' companies.

The LSA

By the early 1960s the London Station Accounts department (LSA), where telegrams were sent primarily for charging account customers, was housed opposite Fleet Building at 32/33 Farringdon Street (currently occupied by Willmott Dixon Interiors and a firm of solicitors, Lloyd Rehman & Co.). In its days as an 'overseas telegraph' building, it sported a brass plate to the left of the front entrance announcing the 'Data Conversion Section'. In its heyday it housed around 400 accounts staff, mostly female, and the main machine in use in those pre-computer days was the comptometer, an electric mechanical calculator or adding machine.

(The LSA, 32/33, Farringdon Street)

EHRCA

The Electra House Retired Colleagues Association is a thriving organisation, founded in 1983 to unite ex-OTOs, engineers and other Electra House staff with fond memories of their days at Cable and Wireless, Post Office Overseas Telegraphs and latterly British Telecom and BT International. The association issues four quarterly newsletters to subscribers, and four social gatherings per year are held in February, May, August and November in London. The current venue for the meetings is *The Crosse Keys*, a large Wetherspoon's pub-restaurant in Gracechurch Street in the City of London, close to the site of an Elizabethan inn of the same name where William Shakespeare and his fellow players once performed. More information about the organisation can be obtained from the secretary, Mr. D. G. Parry at davenaud@btinternet.com, or via the website www.ehrca.co.uk.

Further reading

K. C. Baglehole, O.B.E., *A Century of Service – A Brief History of Cable and Wireless Ltd. 1868 – 1968*, 50pp, Cable and Wireless Ltd (1969)

A. Bailey, I. E. Shircore, *One World – The History of British Telecom 1981 – 91,* 111pp, British Telecom (1991) (exactly 10,082 copies were produced and presented to all serving BT staff)

Hugh Barty-King, *Girdle Round the Earth – The Story of Cable and Wireless*, 413pp, Heinemann, London (1979)

Lt.-Col. Chetwode Crawley M.I.E.E., *From Telegraphy to Television – The Story of Electrical Communications*, 212pp, Frederick Warne and Co. (1931)

Alan Clinton, *Post Office Workers – A Trade Union and Social History*, 713pp, George Allen & Unwin, London (1984)

Charles Graves, *The Thin Red Lines,* 183pp, Standard Art Book Club, London (1946)

A. G. Hobbs, E. W. Yeomanson & A. C. Gee, *Teleprinter Handbook –* (Second Edition)*,* 360pp, Radio Society of Great Britain, Potters Bar (1983)

John Moyle, *Cornwall's Communications Heritage*, 52pp, Twelveheads Press, Truro (2009)

Steven Roberts, *Distant Writing, A History of the Telegraph Companies in Britain between 1838 and 1868.* Available to view on line only, at www.distantwriting.co.uk

Linda Rosenkrantz, *TELEGRAM! – Modern history as told through more than 400 witty, poignant, and revealing telegrams*, 208pp, Henry Holt and Company, New York (2003)

David Souden, *Voices over the Horizon – Tales from Cable and Wireless,* Granta Editions, Cambridge (1999)

Tom Standage, *The Victorian Internet – The Remarkable Story of the Telegraph and the Nineteenth Century's Online Pioneers.* 216pp, Wiedenfeld & Nicolson (1998)

Tim Wander, *MARCONI on the Isle of Wight,* 34pp, TRW Design & Print (2000)

Richard Anthony Young, *The Flying Bomb*, 160pp, Ian Allan Ltd. (1978)

Known related film footage

Spanning the World (1930s Cable and Wireless B & W short)

Destination World (July 1957 Cable & Wireless B & W, 20 minutes)(The film shows young recruits from around the world training at Porthcurno prior to being stationed overseas)

A Modern Miracle (1942 B & W, 4 minutes, 30 seconds) (directed by Desmond Dickinson and made by The Strand Film Company) (Amongst other things the film charts the progress of a telegram sent by a mother in war-torn London to her soldier son serving in North Africa)

The Mountbattens visit Electra House (14/11/1946 B & W, 3 minutes, 24 seconds) (Filmed by Gaumont British News and screened in British cinemas 17/11/46) It portrays their visit to London Station to witness the inauguration of the facsimile service between London and Malta, and to congratulate staff for their war work in the Far East under Mountbatten's command.

On Empire Day, 24th May 1947, the BBC television cameras visited Electra House to film operations in the 'Instrument and Photo-telegraph Rooms' between 8.30 and 9.15 pm - a 25-minute broadcast with a 13 minute interval between the two parts. Programme presenter Freddie Grisewood showed viewers pictures being transmitted to and being received from Cape Town, after which he exchanged greetings by radio-telephone with the Mayor of that city. No known film of the event survives.

Scenes for a film entitled *This Modern Age* were shot at Electra House in June 1948 and featured Sheila J. Sheard and R. Ford Liles operating the London to Athens circuit. No known footage survives.

A documentary entitled *Voices Under The Sea* was shot in 1951 on the *CS Norseman*, at Electra House and at Porthcurno, which doubled for Ascension Island in the film. It was directed by Maurice Harvey, and was released the following year. (B & W, 19 minutes)

Miss GPO Interflora Personality Girl competition featuring Hilda Ferguson, OTO, as the winning finalist of three. (1964 B & W 12 minutes) With brief scenes of her arriving at the main entrance to Electra House and at work, with narration by Kenneth Horne.

Automatic Telegraph Exchange (1968 British Pathé, B & W, silent) (1 minute 20 seconds). Shot at Cardinal House, the film shows external view, operators at an MRC console, the MRC system in operation, a teleprinter in action, etc) (http://www.britishpathe.com/video/automatic-telegraph-
exchange/query/automatic+telegraph)

Three short colour snippets exist from BBC News on 19th, 20th and 21st January 1969, showing various strikers, union pickets, etc, with close-up shots of the closed bronze main doors to Electra House, along with views of the doorway and statues of Mercury on their columns.

Oliver Tommy Oliver (1970 Martin Benson Productions, Colour) (22 minutes) Showing training of OTOs at Cardinal House and Electra House.

The Way it Was (Programme No. 40) (1980s) Grampian TV programme incorporating some footage from *Destination World* (see above)

ILLUSTRATIONS

Pages   1, 14, 47, 48, 53, 55, 89, 91, 92, 93, 94, 95, 97, 99, 100, 102,
           103, 104, 106, 114, 117, 122, 126, 127, 131, 133, 134, 136, 137,
           140, 145, 164, 175 (upper image), 178, 179, 180, 181, 182, 186,
           187, 192, 193, 196, 197, 198, 199, courtesy BT Digital Archives

Pages   21, 40, 64, 76, 78, 80, 82, 88, 98, 109, courtesy
           Telegraph Museum, Porthcurno

Pages   31, 32 courtesy Peter Fisher, London Metropolitan University

Page   87 courtesy Peter Nutt

Page   119 courtesy Iris & Tony Leah

Page   162 courtesy James Grant Collection

Other images courtesy the author/Public Domain

INDEX